The
Bon Homme Richard

a PROW

MAIN TRUCK

i CROSSTREE
j ROPE LADDER
k RIGGING
l PORTS

★ THE AMERICAN ADVENTURE SERIES ★

JOHN PAUL JONES

By VINSON BROWN

EMMETT A. BETTS, *Editor*
Director, Betts Reading Clinic
Haverford, Pennsylvania

Illustrations by
JACK MERRYWEATHER

WHEELER PUBLISHING COMPANY
CHICAGO

33 31

THE AMERICAN ADVENTURE SERIES

△

Table of Contents

From Ship's Boy to Midshipman

A Sword for America

Defending Home Waters

The Fighting Ranger

Victory

YOU HAVE *read of the brave deeds of American pioneers in the forests, on the mountains, and across the plains. But others found adventure on the seas. Of these John Paul Jones was the most famous.*

John Paul was a Scotch gardener's son. But his early love for the sea caused him to become a sailor. Later, he joined the Americans in their fight for justice and freedom. His skill and daring at sea helped win American independence in the Revolutionary War.

John Paul Jones was at his best when he faced danger. His refusal to accept defeat became the spirit of the navy. He earned the proud title, "Father of the American Navy."

VINSON BROWN
EMMETT A. BETTS

The Call of the Sea

"I'LL THANK you, Mr. Mate, to take in two feet on that sail."

"Aye, aye, sir!"

"Steer her close to the enemy!"

"Close to the enemy she is, sir."

The clear voice that called these commands belonged to a boy of thirteen. The deck under the boy's spread legs was part of a sixteen-foot fishing boat. She had one patched sail. But John Paul walked her deck like an admiral.

The boat swung under a high rock, reaching out above the water. An old, empty house stood on the edge of this cliff.

"Is your gun ready, Lieutenant?" asked John.

"Not yet, sir."

The boys in the boat began the task of loading their home-made cannon. It was a length of

1

iron pipe, wrapped with wire and string. One end was sealed with a screw cap. The boys poured gunpowder into the pipe. They stuffed wads of paper on the powder. On the paper they placed a one-inch metal ball. Last of all, one boy poured a line of gunpowder across the deck. The trail of powder led to a tiny hole in the base of the cannon.

"Ready, lads! Stand by, Lieutenant," John ordered. "Fire when your gun is aimed."

John Paul stood very straight and stiff, watching. The lieutenant touched a lighted candle to the trail of gunpowder.

Flame flashed across the deck. The cannon roared. Breaking timbers crashed as the cannon ball hit the empty house. A wall came tumbling down the face of the cliff. The timbers splashed into the waters of the bay. They tossed foam on the young warriors.

"A hit!" yelled John Paul, waving his cap.

"Hurrah! Hurrah!" the boys cheered.

"Put her about!" John Paul ordered.

"Aye, aye, sir."

"Stand by your stations, lads!" John Paul commanded. "We'll fire again, if she doesn't haul her colors."

John Paul and his friends were making believe that they were fighting another ship at sea. To "haul her colors" meant that the enemy ship would pull down her flag and give up the fight.

Just then a woman's voice called from the shore. "John! John Paul!" The woman on the beach waved her hand.

"Yes, Mother."

"Bring in your boat! Come home! I have news for you."

John Paul turned to the boy who was steering the boat. "You are playing the part of the quartermaster," he said. "We have orders waiting for us. Swing her about again, Quartermaster! Make sail for home!"

"Aye, aye, sir."

The young quartermaster obeyed. When the little boat reached the harbor, John Paul quickly jumped ashore. He raced up a short cut through the village to his home.

John Paul lived on the coast of southern Scotland. His father worked for a rich man who owned a great house. There were beautiful gardens around the house. John Paul's father cared for the gardens. He and his family lived in a small stone house near by.

John Paul often worked with his father in the gardens. He spaded flower beds and trained vines. He planted seeds and set bulbs. He cut grass and raked leaves. The boy did his work well, but he often paused to look out to sea.

One day, John Paul's father spoke to the boy. "My lad," he said, "you do like to work in the gardens, don't you?"

The boy's answer was a long time coming. He stood gazing at the fresh-turned earth of the bed he was spading. At last he lifted his eyes to meet his father's anxious gaze.

"Yes, I like to work in the gardens, but—"

"I'm glad to hear you say that, Son," his father broke in. "Some day you may take my place here. I have hoped since you were a little lad that you would be a gardener, too. Your mother and

I often speak of what it would mean to have you with us as we grow old."

John stood silent, looking out over the sea. After a pause he said, "I do like to work with plants. I like to be with you and mother. But I can't stay here and be a gardener. I can't, Father, because something out there is calling me."

The boy flung his arm in a wide sweep toward the blue waters breaking on the coast.

John Paul saw the hurt look on his father's face. "Please try to understand, Father," he begged. "I'd like to do as you wish, but I have to go to sea. More than anything in the world I want to be a sailor."

The man dropped his hand on the boy's arm. "It's all right, lad," he said. "You must do the work that your heart calls you to do."

John Paul lifted his chin and threw back his shoulders. "Some day I'll be captain of a ship," he boasted. "Then I'll come sailing home to see you and mother."

John Paul's father at last saw that his son

would be happy only on a ship. He then asked the man for whom he worked to help the lad.

The man agreed to find the boy a place on a ship. He suggested that John Paul might be appointed to the English Navy. In the navy he would receive training as an officer. The young men in training to become officers were called midshipmen. John Paul could think of nothing more wonderful than to be a midshipman.

Now John Paul was sure that there was news about his going to sea. Nearing the little stone house, he saw his mother talking to a man. It was the gentleman who had promised to help him. The boy's heart skipped a beat. He ran faster.

"Oh, sir," he asked, standing before the man, "did you get a job for me?"

"Yes," the man nodded, "as a ship's boy. Do you know what a ship's boy has to do?"

"Oh, yes, sir," John Paul beamed. "I will have to clean the captain's cabin. I'll help the cook, too. And I'll carry messages for the mate, and do all sorts of sea jobs."

The boy spread his legs wide apart. He held himself as though he were standing on the deck of a ship. He asked, "When do I sail?"

"Tomorrow," the man answered. "You'll cross the bay to Whitehaven, and sail from there, I—"

"So soon?" broke in John Paul's mother. "So soon? Couldn't he have a little more time before he leaves?"

The gentleman shook his head. "The merchant who owns the ship is a friend of mine. I want your son to work for him. He is kind to his men. Many ship owners are not. I don't want John to work on their ships."

"What is the name of the vessel?" asked John Paul.

"The *Friendship*."

"Where is she sailing?"

"To America."

"America," whispered John Paul. "America!" He repeated the word as if it were magic.

And to the poor Scotch boy of 1760, America was a magic name. John Paul had heard much of this new land across the sea. He knew that settlers in America sometimes grew rich. He knew, too, that they enjoyed many rights and even made some of their own laws.

The freedom in America seemed very wonderful to John Paul. His own country, Scotland, had been conquered by England some years before John was born.

The proud Scotch people had loved their freedom. They were not happy under the stern English rule. Many of them left Scotland to seek their fortunes in other lands.

John Paul's older brother, William, had gone to America. He had settled in Fredericksburg, Virginia. William wrote glowing letters about the country and the people. A man who was willing to work hard was very likely to succeed. William, starting with nothing, had become a tailor and was doing very well, indeed.

"Oh, Mother," said John Paul, "think of it! I am going to America."

Seeing the tears in her eyes, the boy pleaded, "Don't change your mind now, Mother. You promised me that I could go. You promised."

His mother smiled down at him. He was too
young to go, too young to leave home. But she
said nothing. She saw how eager he was to be
off on the journey. His face glowed with excitement and his eyes flashed with fire.

"I will not break my promise, Son," his mother
said at last. "No matter how hard it will be to
let you go, I will keep my promise."

"You won't be sorry, Mother. I'll make good,
and some day I'll be captain of a fine, big ship.
Some day, I'll take you and father and my sisters
to America. We can all live in Fredericksburg,
Virginia, with William. Wouldn't you like that,
Mother?"

"Yes, my son," his mother replied. "And here
is a surprise for you. You will land at Fredericksburg. You can stay with your brother while
the ship is being loaded for the return voyage."

John Paul turned to the gentleman. "Thank
you, sir," he said. "Thank you for everything. I
will do a good job, sir."

"I am sure you will, John," said the man, holding out his hand. "Good-by and good sailing."

That night John sat a long time before the fire with his father and mother. His father talked of the proud history of Scotland. He spoke of the need for every son of Scotland to prove himself a man of courage and honor.

John's mother showed her concern for the boy. She asked him to take good care of his health. She begged him to remember the manners she had taught him. But most of all, she spoke of her faith in him. She told him that she expected him to become a great and good man.

John Paul liked to boast of the great sailor he would be. But on this last evening at home he did not feel like boasting. There was a lump in his throat. Words did not come easily.

Standing before his mother to say good-night the boy at last found his voice. "This has been a good evening, Mother. I'll remember it always. And I'll remember what you and father have told me, too."

Ship's Boy to America

EARLY THE next morning, John Paul was on his way to board the *Friendship*. He carried a new sea bag in his hand and high hope in his heart.

The lad took a boat which carried him to Whitehaven. On the trip across the bay, he gazed at the village of his birth. The mist along the shore was lifting under the bright rays of the sun.

He took a long, last look at the great cliffs and green valleys of Scotland. They were beautiful, and Scotland was home. But John Paul turned and squared his shoulders. He knew, somehow, that he was going to like America better.

Whitehaven was a busy place. Officers hurried along the streets. Sailors sang as they went about their tasks. The harbor was full of ships. The tall timbers, or masts, that supported the sails

12

swayed in the breeze. The sails sparkled in the sunshine. The hammers of ship builders went rat-a-tat-tat.

The stir and hum made John Paul want to put to sea at once. But he must first report to the merchant on whose ship he was sailing.

The merchant had a store on the main street of Whitehaven. The store was piled high with goods from lands beyond the sea. There were silks and spices, cotton and tobacco. The merchant was a tall bean-pole of a man with a face like a horse. But his brown eyes twinkled.

"So you are going to be a ship's boy to my firm, are you, young man?" he asked.

"Yes, sir," John said.

"Well, those long arms of yours ought to help you climb rope ladders. Let me feel your muscle. Ho! Ho! You are hard as iron. Where did you get that muscle?"

"I have been doing garden work," John said. "And I've helped the fishermen with their boats, when I had a chance, sir. I know a lot about boats and the sea."

"What about your schooling, young man? Can you read and write and use figures?"

"Yes, sir. My teacher taught me all of that."

"Good! Good! Keep studying, boy. We might make a captain out of you some day. That is, we might, if you are willing to study for it."

"That's what I am going to be, sir, a captain on a ship-of-war."

"Ho! Ho! A young warrior, are you? Well, you had better not tell that to your captain. He has been in the King's Navy. He says you work like a slave, and get paid about the same. But— here is the captain now. Ho, Captain!"

A huge red-faced man in an officer's uniform came rolling into the store. His eyes twinkled at the small lad standing so stiff and straight.

"Is this my ship's boy?" roared the captain.

"Yes, Captain," answered the merchant, "and I have a feeling he will be a good one."

"We shall see," said the captain. "What do you do when you reef a sail, lad?"

"You roll it up and tie it on the cross-stick on the mast, sir."

"And what is the cross-stick?" the captain continued.

"It's a piece of wood or metal fastened across the mast to hold up the sail."

"That is right." The captain beamed. "We shall give you a chance to do some reefing." He turned to the merchant. "Get this boy down to the ship at once."

"All right, Captain," said the merchant. "John Paul, take your sea bag and hurry down to the *Friendship*. Go south two blocks and turn left. She will be at the end of the street."

"Ask for the mate, my lad," said the captain. "He will show you where to put your bag."

John Paul was away in a flash. He wanted to get his brand new sea bag put out of sight on the ship.

"A new bag is a sure give away," John Paul said to himself. "Everyone who sees it will know I'm going to sea for the first time. But if I can get it aboard before the fellows see it, I'll be all right. I can rough it up a bit and make it look like an old bag."

But John Paul's plan did not work. He met a pair of sailors looking for some fun.

"Where are you going?" one sailor called. "Are you a pirate?"

"No, sir."

"That sea bag is so stiff and new she will walk with you, if you let her!"

The two seamen roared with laughter. People passing on the street smiled. John Paul hurried on.

He found the *Friendship* at the end of the street. She was a three-masted vessel. Her clean lines delighted John Paul. He thrilled at sight of the openings in the ship's sides. He knew that behind those ports, heavy iron cannon were hidden.

John Paul stepped quickly up the plank that led to the ship. At the end of the gangplank he was met by a round-faced officer.

"Well, well, our new ship's boy!" the man cried in a hearty voice. "I'm the mate."

"How do you do, sir."

"Fit as a fiddle and ready for sea." The mate grinned. "I have had all the land I can stand for awhile. But come, boy, I'll show you where to stow your bag. Then you can meet the crew."

The mate led John Paul to a tiny space near the stern, or rear, of the ship. The space was so low that the boy could not stand in it. There was a cloth sack full of dry hay to sleep on. John Paul thought it was fine. He was glad to have a place all to himself. He crawled in to "stow his gear," as a sailor says when he puts away his belongings.

John Paul heard sailors singing. He knew that the place where they slept would be up in the bow, or front, of the ship. He crawled out of his cubbyhole and started forward to look for the crew's quarters.

A queer, sinking feeling came into John Paul's stomach. He didn't feel easy. He kept remembering that he was going to sea for the first time. Thoughts of home flashed through his mind. He recalled the look on his mother's face when she told him good-by. For a moment, he wished himself back home. But a look at the ship made his heart once more leap with joy.

The men were not in their quarters after all. The new ship's boy found them on the deck. The entire crew of sixteen seamen were taking a rest.

"Here comes the new ship's boy," a clear voice sounded. The sailors turned to stare.

"What's your name, boy?" a man asked.

"John Paul."

"First time to sea?"

"Yes, sir."

A sailor winked broadly. "Let's test him," he suggested.

"Boy," said a leather-faced seaman, "I am Dirk Robinson. I want to help you."

"Yes, sir. Thank you, sir," John Paul swallowed a lump in his throat.

Grinning at his friends, the seaman asked, "Do you know what a landlubber is?"

"Oh, yes, sir," the boy replied. "It's someone who always stays on land."

"Well," Dirk continued, "if you don't want to be a landlubber, you must learn to act like a sailor. The captain will order a light put on the main-truck. Do you know where that is?"

John Paul spoke slowly. "I, I think I know."
"Show us where it is then."

All eyes were fastened on John Paul. His
heart beat rapidly. He knew that the main-truck
was the very tiptop of the largest mast, or mainmast. But he did not let on that he knew. He
decided to play a trick on the crew. He thought
he could prove to them that he was no landlubber.

In front of the mainmast is the foremast. Rope
ladders extend from the foremast to the deck on
either side of the ship. Sailors use the ladders
when they climb the foremast.

Far above the deck pieces of wood or metal are
fastened across the foremast. These pieces are
called the crosstrees. Heavy ropes extend between
the foremast and the mainmast. Other ropes extend from the masts to the deck. The ropes help
to hold the tall masts steady.

John Paul walked over to a rope ladder. He
began to climb very slowly toward the foremast.

Glancing down, he saw smiles widen on the
faces of the sailors.

The boy soon came to the place where the rope

ladder led straight up the mast. He began to inch his way upward. Once he seemed to slip.

"I hope they think I'm terribly scared," John said to himself.

When the lad reached the crosstrees, he started out on them. Far below, he saw the sailors. They were gathered now in a tight knot. Every face was turned upward, watching. Inch by inch, the boy pulled himself out on the crosstrees.

Suddenly, from below came a hoarse voice, "Don't do it, boy! Don't do it!"

John Paul grinned, and crawled on. Then he seemed to lose his hold on the crosstrees. He gave a cry and started to drop. But he seized the tip of a crosstree and hung there in the air.

Shouts came from the deck. A sailor yelled at Dirk, "You and your funny ideas! You are going to kill the boy."

"Robinson," the mate's voice roared, "get up there! Get that lad before he kills himself."

"Aye, aye, sir."

Robinson leaped up the rope ladders. His face was gray with fright.

John Paul let the seaman come within twenty feet. Then, he arched his body like a bow, and was away! He leaped from the crosstrees onto the ropes that extend from foremast to mainmast. He went swinging across them like a monkey on a trailing vine. Reaching the mainmast, he climbed to the tip of it. Then, he turned around, and grinned at the open-mouthed Dirk. "Is this the main-truck you wanted me to reach, Mr. Robinson?" he asked.

"Yes," gasped Dirk.

John Paul caught hold of a rope fastened to the mainmast. He slid down the rope to the deck. He came almost fast enough to burn his hands, but not quite. He knew that trick, too. The crew broke into wild cheering.

Dirk Robinson tumbled down a rope ladder. He seized the lad's hand and shook it warmly.

"I'll thrash the first man who calls our ship's boy a landlubber," he cried.

"Ho! Ho!" the men laughed. "You'll never hear us call John Paul a landlubber. He's a born sailor!"

The Great Green Land

"ALL HANDS on deck!" roared the captain's deep voice. John Paul sat up with a start. His sleepy eyes saw the gray light of early morning. The ship had lain in port over night. Now she was going out with the tide.

The ship's boy rolled out of his cubbyhole. He heard the mate singing out orders to the seamen.

John Paul reached the deck to find men setting the sails. They did this by pulling ropes that were fastened to the masts and sails. This network of ropes was called the rigging of the ship. The men worked quickly. The sails dropped down and filled in the wind.

The big iron anchor that held the vessel in place was lifted. The *Friendship* slipped out into the harbor, and headed for America.

His first day at sea, John Paul was everywhere, watching and helping. If a man needed a rope, John brought it. If a sailor tied a knot, John's eyes followed every turn of the sailor's hands. He whistled when he scrubbed grease off the stove. He did odd jobs in double-quick time.

That night, John Paul crawled into his cubbyhole. His weary legs ached, but his mind whirled with thoughts. He went over the happenings of the day. His mind leaped ahead to the adventures before him. He thrilled at the thought of learning to mend ropes and reef sails. His heart pounded when he remembered the great guns.

"I'm only a ship's boy now. But some day I'll be captain of a warship." John Paul made himself this promise in a fierce whisper.

John Paul's days at sea were all busy ones. He did his own tasks well. He asked the seamen eager questions about their work. Dirk Robinson became his special friend and teacher. Dirk taught John to tie many kinds of knots. He showed the boy how to weave the threads of two ropes together into a splice.

The ship's boy liked to climb high on the masts. Better still, he liked to ride a mast in rough weather. At such a time, the ship dipped her blunt nose into the great waves. The mast swayed out over the ocean. Then the ship rocked back to the other side. Mast and boy swept through the air in a wide, thrilling curve.

One day, John Paul was high on a mast gazing across the tumbling waves. He shaded his eyes with one hand, and peered toward the west.

"I'd like to be the first to sight land," he thought. "I can hardly wait to see America. William's letters say it's a wonderful place. If it is, I am going to make America my home."

The boy thought over the two promises he had made himself. His straight brows came together in a frown. He spoke aloud in a puzzled voice.

"I want to be captain on a warship. I want to live in America. But America is not a nation. It belongs to Britain, so it has no warships."

John Paul sighed. He began to climb slowly down the rope ladder. Reaching the deck, he stood a moment gazing out to sea.

"I know the two things I want to do," he told himself. "It looks as if I can't do both of them. But I will do both. I'll find a way, or make one."

Days turned into weeks. The big cannon still lay hidden behind the ports. Since the start of the voyage, they hadn't been used. John Paul went to the mate.

"Sir," he asked, "when are we going to practice with the guns?"

"Why, bless me, lad! You are too small to work with one of those guns."

"Oh, no, I'm not, sir. And I need to learn how to fire the guns, sir."

The mate looked at the slender boy before him. He broke into a laugh. "And why do you think you need to learn?" he asked.

"Because I expect to command a battleship."

The mate's face grew sober, but his eyes held a twinkle. "If you are to command a man-of-war you should learn to handle guns," he agreed. "And, as a matter of fact, the men probably need gun practice, too. I'll speak to the captain about holding a gun drill."

"Why, yes," said the captain, when the mate spoke to him. "The men need it. Take charge of the drill."

A little later the mate's great voice shouted an order. "All hands on deck!"

Some men rushed up from below deck. Others hurried down the rigging. They lined up before the mate, and stood waiting for further orders. John Paul watched Dirk, and did as he did.

The guns were placed on both sides of the ship. Those on the right side, or starboard, were called the starboard guns. Those on the left side, or larboard, were called the larboard guns. All of them were tied, or as the sailors say, lashed, in place with ropes.

"Clear starboard guns for action!" the mate ordered. The men rushed to the guns and began to unlash the ropes. John Paul was in Dirk's gun crew. He rushed with the others to help.

Each of the big iron guns had a four-inch mouth, or muzzle. The gun was mounted on runners. The runners fitted into narrow channels, or grooves, in the deck. When the crew had a gun

free of its lashings the men pushed it forward.
The gun was ready to fire when its muzzle
pointed out through the open port.

"Five minutes, fifty-eight seconds," the mate
complained. "On a man-of-war, seamen make a
gun ready in two and a half minutes, or less.
They have the guns loaded, too. You men are
slow. Do it again. Clear the larboard guns!"

The men charged to the left side of the ship.
They opened the ports, freed the guns, and thrust
them out.

"Four minutes, fifty seconds," said the mate.
"That's better."

The men rested briefly. John Paul asked eager
questions about the use of the guns in battle.

"On a man-of-war," Dirk explained, "boys
spread sand on the deck."

"Why?"

"The sand soaks up the blood of the wounded."

"What else do boys do on battleships?"

"They bring buckets of water and put them beside every gun. The water is used to clean the
guns," Dirk said.

"We'll practice once with the guns loaded," called the mate. "Load for action, but use powder only."

A tub of candle grease stood by each gun. A long string dipped into this grease was called a match.

"Here lad," said the mate to John Paul, "see that the matches in the tubs are lighted."

"Aye, aye, sir," John replied.

The men rushed to get loads of gunpowder. They loaded the guns down the muzzles. To do this, they first poured a quantity of powder into each muzzle. This powder was called a charge. Next, they put in a wad of paper. Then, with a long rod, called a ramrod, they pushed the paper and powder into place. They spread a trail of powder across the deck. This trail led to the charge in the loaded gun. The gun was fired by touching the trail of powder with a lighted match.

"Ready to open fire, sir," each gunner's mate called when his gun was ready.

"Fire!" roared the mate. He brought his arm down in a mighty sweep.

Flames shot from the muzzles. The guns roared. Smoke drifted away from the ship in great puffs. John Paul stood beside a gun, his eyes blazing.

"All right, men, close the ports. Lash back the guns," ordered the mate. The gun drill was over. But John Paul still watched the puffs of white smoke. A strange feeling of power had come over him when the guns roared.

There were other gun drills. In time, John Paul knew each move that he was expected to make. He did his work well. One day, the captain paused to speak a word of praise at the close of a drill.

He said, "Some day you'll be the best gunner on the *Friendship*."

"Thank you, sir," John replied. "And there's something I'd like to ask you, sir."

"What is it, my boy?"

"Would you teach me how to steer and handle a ship? I need to know that, too."

"So you want to learn navigation," the captain said. "That will be a long, hard pull. You will have to burn the midnight oil, lad. You have to study to be a navigator."

"I will study very hard, sir," said John Paul. "I want to learn everything about handling a ship. Everything!"

One day, John was high up on the crosstrees reefing a sail. Since early morning he had been straining his eyes looking into the west. Suddenly, what he thought was gray mist looked solid.

"Land ho!" he shouted.

"Where away?" the captain roared from below.

"Dead ahead, sir."

The captain ran up the rope ladder to have a look. He put his spyglass to his eye.

"It's Virginia," he said. "Keep your eyes open, lad. Watch for a bay." The captain went below.

"I see the bay," called John Paul a few minutes later. "It's over there, sir." He pointed to the left of the course that the ship was following.

Again the captain came up to look. "Yes, you are right," he agreed.

"Lay her course west-south-west," the captain shouted to the quartermaster.

"West-south-west she is, sir."

The *Friendship* changed her course slightly to

larboard. The wind whined through her rigging.

John Paul came below. But often he ran up the rope ladder for another look. The gray shape slowly changed into a long, low, green coast line. The ship neared the opening of the bay.

"What bay is it?" John asked Dirk.

"Chesapeake Bay, lad. We sail up the bay until we come to the Rappahannock River. Then we sail up the river to Fredericksburg."

Two days later, the ship reached Fredericksburg. A crowd lined the river banks. Workmen in leather jackets and breeches pushed forward eagerly. A little apart stood a group of gentlemen. They were dressed in gaily-colored velvet coats, ruffled shirts, knee-breeches, and silver-buckled shoes. Other men in suits of sober brown were standing along the banks.

John Paul pressed against the deck rail gazing at the crowd. He had not seen William for several years. There had been no time to write his brother of his coming. But he hoped that William might happen to meet the ship. Now, the boy studied the faces, but all seemed strange.

The look of hope faded on John Paul's face. Then, he caught sight of a tall man in a well-cut suit. The man's walk reminded John of his father. He looked more closely at the stranger.

"That could be William," John Paul thought.

The ship's boy was down the gangplank in a flash. He darted quickly through the crowd, and stopped beside the man. "Please, sir," he asked "could you be Mr. William Paul?"

The man looked down in puzzled surprise. "I could be, and I am," he replied.

"Oh, I'm glad, sir, that is, William, I mean." The lad stopped, too excited to say more. After a moment, he added, "I'm glad I found you."

"I don't think I understand."

"Why, I'm John, I'm John Paul, your brother."

The puzzled look on the man's face gave place to surprise and joy. Cupping the boy's face in his hands, the man studied it with hungry eyes. "My little brother!" he cried. "Of course, you are my little brother. But how did you get here?"

John Paul frowned at the words, "little brother." He drew himself up as tall as he could.

"I'm not little, William," he said. "I'm thirteen years old and ship's boy on the *Friendship*."

William held out his right hand. Taking his brother's hand, he shook it warmly. "I beg pardon, John," he said. "You have earned the right to be called a man—and a seaman at that."

John Paul's face lighted. "Thank you, William. A seaman is what I want to be more than anything. And some day, I'm going to be a ship's captain, too."

William Paul smiled. "Welcome to America, Captain-to-be, John Paul," he said. "You have the spirit we like here in the new world. I can see you're going to be a real American."

---

1. What new skills did John learn on his first voyage?
2. Trace the route of John's first voyage on a map.
3. Draw a picture of a three-masted ship. On it mark the *mainmast, foremast, rigging, crosstrees,* and *main-truck.*
4. Why did the seamen call John "a born sailor"?

Midshipman to the King

THE *Friendship* was tied up at Fredericksburg for several weeks. The vessel was loaded with tobacco and grain. Supplies for the voyage home were stowed away on board.

John Paul was glad of the *Friendship's* long stay at Fredericksburg. He lived at his brother's house, and explored the little town.

The ship's boy found it a busy place. Coaches rolled up to the inns. Wagons rattled along the streets. Ships rode at anchor in the river.

The day came at last for the *Friendship* to sail. John Paul was more sorry than glad. He wanted to stay longer in America.

"I'll be back," John said to William. "I like this new land. I want to see more of it."

In the next six years, John Paul did return to America on several voyages. Each time that his ship put in, the boy went ashore. He visited often in William's home.

One day, William Paul said, "John, you had better decide to settle in America."

"I've thought of doing that," John answered. "America is like a second home to me. I love it here. But I love the sea, too."

John Paul's ship sailed between England and America. When it was in an English harbor, John always went home to visit. One day, he arrived in Scotland to find his mother much excited.

"I've wonderful news for you, John," she cried.

"What is it, Mother?"

"You have been appointed a midshipman in the King's Navy."

John Paul threw his cap into the air. "Hurrah!" he shouted. "Hurrah! At last I'm on my way toward becoming a captain."

"Your father and I are very proud of you." John's mother gazed fondly at her son. Then she added, "And we shall never cease to thank the kind gentleman who has helped you."

The boy nodded. "Nor will I. He secured the place on the *Friendship* for me. And I know that I owe this new chance to him, too."

"Yes, he asked a friend of his to have you appointed a midshipman."

"I'll do my best to be worthy of his faith in me," John Paul promised.

The mother's face clouded. "There's one thing that I don't like," she sighed.

"What is that, Mother?"

"You will have such a short time at home. You must go aboard ship at Plymouth, England, one week from today."

The new midshipman reported to the King's ship, the *Sphinx*. Coming aboard ship, John Paul was met by the first lieutenant. John Paul noticed the officer's firm chin. He thought that the lieutenant would be a bad enemy to have in a fight. But a look at the officer's kind eyes told John more. He knew that the lieutenant would also be a fair fighter.

The officer looked at a list of names that he held in his hand.

"Mr. John Paul, I believe," the officer soon remarked.

"Yes, sir." John Paul stood very straight and tipped his cap.

"A midshipman will show you to your quarters," the lieutenant continued.

The lieutenant glanced down the deck. "James!" he called.

A boy left a group of midshipmen, and came running. He was a pale-faced lad of about sixteen.

"James, this is Mr. Midshipman Paul. Show him to his quarters."

The boy touched his hat. He nodded to John Paul. "Follow me," he said.

John Paul followed, carrying his sea bag. The other midshipmen, gathered on deck, stared at him. One big fellow gave him an ugly look. John Paul didn't like that look. But he soon forgot it in the joy of seeing his first warship.

The *Sphinx* was a light ship-of-war. Such a ship was called a frigate. Though it was not a heavy battleship, it looked very wonderful to John Paul. Iron cannon were lashed in place. Ropes lay neatly coiled. Every piece of brass shone like a polished mirror. Seamen in stiff white uniforms went about their duties. Soldiers of the sea, called marines, stood by the rails, guns in hand.

James led John Paul to the midshipmen's quarters. These were two small, dark rooms. They were inside, or in the hold, of the ship.

John saw that the quarters were already crowded. His swinging bed, or hammock, would take up the last bit of space. He began moving other sea bags to make a place for his bag.

"Brains won't like it, if you move his bag," said James.

"Brains?" asked John Paul.

"He is that big fellow you saw on deck. He's a bully, and he's king of the midshipmen's quarters. Brains has an uncle who is a nobleman. That makes him lord it over the rest of us."

"I don't care who he is," said John Paul. "There isn't very much room, but I have a right to my share."

"Brains won't like it." James repeated the warning, but there was respect in his voice.

The boy looked at John Paul. He admired John's well-built figure. He noticed that John's five feet six inches were all solid bone and muscle. He saw the long arms and powerful wrists of the new midshipman.

John Paul stowed away his sea bag in the space he had made.

"Tell me," he asked, "what do midshipmen do on this ship?"

"We have old Gigs to teach us," said James.

"Who is Gigs?"

"He is a funny old fellow who teaches us history and mathematics. He tries to make gentlemen of us, too," James laughed. "He is supposed to prepare us for the examinations."

"Doesn't he?"

"Oh, he tries. But there's only one midshipman who listens to him. The examinations don't mean very much." James laughed again. "Only the boys who belong to important families are made officers anyway."

"Who is this midshipman who listens to Gigs?" John Paul asked.

"A little chap named Dave Bonner. He's an American. He hasn't found out yet how things are in the British Navy. Bonner still thinks he'll be promoted to an officer's rank, if he works hard. But he'll learn."

John Paul did not like the ideas that James was suggesting. He hated to believe that only boys from noble families could be promoted.

"What else do you do?" John Paul asked.

"Well, we take turns watching on deck when we are at sea. But this guard duty is not too bad. The seamen do the dirty work for us. And, of course, we are supposed to practice with the guns. But we only do that when we feel like it. We spend most of our time baiting the seamen."

"What do you mean by 'baiting the seamen'?"

"Oh, we go around making them mad, so they won't salute us. That is what we call 'baiting.' Brains Dorgan is good at it."

"What happens if they don't salute?"

At this moment, there came the sound of a struggle on deck. Midshipman James grinned.

"Come on," he laughed. "You will see."

John Paul and the boy ran up to the main deck.
A struggling sailor was being held by four other
seamen. Midshipman Dorgan stood before him.
The big midshipman's face was an angry red.

"What is going on here?" an officer roared. At
the sound the fighting sailor stopped struggling.

"This sailor refused to salute me, sir," Dorgan
answered. "He almost struck me."

John Paul saw that the officer wore the uniform of a captain. His heart sank when he studied
the man's beef-red face. He did not like what he
saw in the captain's little black eyes. He liked
still less the tone of the captain's voice.

"Speak up, man! Is this true?" the captain
snarled.

"Yes, sir," the sailor answered.

The first lieutenant came up to the group.

He said, "It is possible, sir, that Midshipman
Dorgan started the trouble. I hear that he baited
this seaman."

"Baited him, bosh!" growled the captain. "What
if he did bait him? We should have a man hauled
underneath the ship for striking at an officer.

But I'll be easy on him this time. He shall have a whipping instead. Give him two dozen lashes, Lieutenant."

"Aye, aye, sir."

The lieutenant's face was troubled. He looked at Midshipman Dorgan with angry eyes.

"All hands on deck to witness punishment!" the lieutenant snapped.

Sailors and marines lined up. They formed three sides of a hollow square. Officers and midshipmen filled the fourth side of the square. The captain took his position on the upper, or quarter deck.

The sailor's shirt was stripped from his back. His hands were tied together, and lifted high against the mast. This caused the man to stand nearly on his toes.

The task of whipping sailors was a duty of one of the officers of lower rank. This officer was called the boatswain. He now came forward, whip in hand.

The boatswain struck suddenly with great force. Red marks appeared on the man's back.

His body bent under the blow. But no sound came from between his tight lips. The marine drummers rolled out a steady booming on the drums. The boatswain's arm lifted and fell again.

John Paul heard a sigh and glanced around. He saw a black-haired boy about thirteen years old turning his head away. The other midshipmen were watching the punishment with wide grins on their faces.

John Paul lost count of the blows. He closed his eyes, sick at heart. Once he heard the first lieutenant say, "You don't have to lay it on so heavy, Boatswain."

In a little while, the whipping was over. The man had fainted without a sound. A seaman threw a bucket of salt water over him. Two other seamen carried him away.

John Paul turned to the young boy he had noticed. "You must be Dave Bonner," he said.

"I am, but how did you know my name?"

"James told me about you. He said you are an American. I am glad you are on board. I've been to America and I like its people."

Dave Bonner held out his hand, "How glad I am to find you," he cried. "Tell me all about yourself."

The two midshipmen fell into a long talk. At length, John Paul asked, "How did you become a midshipman?"

"The King allowed the colonies two midshipmen in the navy this year," Dave Bonner answered. "Dr. Benjamin Franklin had me appointed to one of the places."

"I wish America had a navy. I'd be in it," John Paul said.

"And so would I," young Dave Bonner agreed.

John Paul went about his new duties quietly. Every time he looked up he found Midshipman Dorgan watching him. The big fellow's face wore a look of scorn.

That evening, John Paul saw several midshipmen standing in a tight knot. Dorgan was in the center of the group.

The young men talked in low tones. Passing near the group, John heard Dorgan snarl, "Scotch gardener's son."

John Paul was tired from the excitement of his first day on the *Sphinx*. He went to his hammock early and was soon asleep. A bucket of water dashed in his face brought him suddenly awake. He jumped from his hammock, with fists ready to fight. He struck out in the darkness. But there was no enemy before him. Only a scornful laugh met his blows.

———

1. What kind of ship was a frigate? Look in your dictionary to find what has taken her place in the modern navy.

2. Discuss several uses of the word *quarters*.

3. How did John show that he had courage?

Scotch Gardener's Son

THE *Sphinx* put to sea in a stiff wind. The sails were filled with the breeze. The white-capped waves played about the ship.

The first lieutenant came on deck. He studied the spread sails. "I need a man to go up the mast," he stated.

John Paul stepped forward and saluted. "I'd like to go aloft, sir," he said.

"Go up the mainmast. Make a better spread on that highest sail. Flatten it to the wind." The first lieutenant gave his orders briskly.

"Aye, aye, sir."

John Paul jumped for the rope ladder. Up he went, and up, racing like mad. Quickly, he spread the highest sail. It no longer filled with the breeze. In ten seconds he had it flat with the wind. In five seconds more he again stood on the deck. The seamen cheered. But Brains Dorgan gave John a black look.

The hour came for the midshipmen's lessons. The young men marched into the ship's cabin. Old Gigs began to speak.

"Gentlemen," he said, "today we shall discuss the importance of the navy in time of war."

Dorgan stuck his feet up on the table. He yawned loudly. Young James closed his eyes and made believe that he was asleep. The old teacher flushed.

Dave Bonner was seated in front of Gigs. "Please sir —," Dave began. A sharp kick on his leg broke off his speech. "Ouch!" he cried, rubbing his leg. The boy sitting next to Dave grinned.

John Paul leaned over and touched the boy. "I'll thank you to move, sir. I want to hear what the teacher has to say. It seems that you don't. I suggest that you trade chairs with me."

"Why, you!" The boy whirled in his chair and snarled at John Paul. John's steady gaze never left the boy's angry eyes. For a long minute the two midshipmen faced each other. Then the boy's head dropped. Without a word he rose to his feet.

John Paul quietly took the seat next to Dave Bonner. The teacher began the lesson. The eager faces of the two midshipmen gave new spirit to the old man. He started to tell stories about sea fights. John Paul and Dave Bonner broke in with questions.

Gigs face lighted up. His stories grew more lively. In spite of themselves, other midshipmen became interested. They leaned forward in their chairs to listen. Only Brains Dorgan refused to pay attention. He sat in his corner, his face like an angry cloud.

Later in the day, John Paul drew Dave Bonner aside.

"Dave," he said, "there's going to be trouble in the midshipmen's quarters."

"I'm afraid you're right. Brains is furious with you." Dave shook his head sadly.

"That bully and I would be bound to have trouble sooner or later," John Paul said. "It's just as well to have things settled now."

"But he may hurt you," Dave Bonner warned.

"He may, but I don't think so. I've a plan that may teach him a lesson. Will you help me?"

"Of course, I will. I'd like to see the bully put in his place."

"I'm expecting Dorgan to come at me tonight. He will likely wait, though, till he thinks I'm asleep."

"What will we do?" Dave asked.

"After it's dark in the quarters we'll trade hammocks. Then we'll both act as if we were sound asleep. But I'll have a trap waiting for Mr. Brains Dorgan. I learned a few tricks with ropes from a seaman named Dirk Robinson. We'll use some of them tonight."

"You can count on me," Dave said.

"I'll spring my trap before Dorgan has a chance to attack you," John Paul promised.

Four bells sounded. That marked the time on board ship as ten o'clock. The midshipmen were in their hammocks. It was dark as the bottom of the sea in their quarters. Moving on cat's feet, John Paul and Dave Bonner changed hammocks.

The silent minutes stretched into an hour. Then a second hour dragged past. Eight bells struck at midnight. Dave Bonner's breathing was regular and easy.

"Dave's asleep," John Paul said to himself. "Dorgan will be coming soon."

John Paul crawled from the hammock. Without a sound, he moved through the darkness. He bent low to miss touching the other hammocks. His fingers searched the deck.

"Ah, there it is!" he thought, feeling the rope that he had hidden. He found an iron, deck ring near by. "Lucky that ring is here. It will be useful," he said to himself.

John touched each knot carefully. The trap was ready. He stood in the black shadow, and became a part of it.

Minutes later, John Paul heard a faint squeaking. The sound came from his right. A moment later he heard a movement on his left. "They are coming from both sides," he decided.

A soft whisper reached John Paul's sharp ears. "Now, lads, when I give the word, grab him." The voice giving the whispered command belonged to Dorgan.

"No, you don't," John Paul thought.

In a flash, John seized the big midshipman's wrists. He jerked them behind Dorgan before the bully knew what was happening. Grasping Dorgan's wrists in one hand, John seized the rope with his other hand. He slipped a loop over the wrists. John Paul jerked Dorgan to the deck. He ran the end of the rope through the ring.

Dorgan's friends jumped at John Paul. Dave Bonner awakened, and piled into the fight. John held Dorgan down with one hand by pulling on the rope. John struck with his free fist. His knuckles crashed into flesh and bone.

A boy plunged to the deck, and lay there groaning. A second time, John's fist sent a midshipman flying. But this fellow picked himself up, and plunged back into the fight. Dave rushed him. John Paul pounded him. The midshipman dropped under a blow, and crawled away. He did not come back.

The next few minutes were filled with the

sounds of the struggle. There was the smack of fists on flesh. There was the thud of men hitting the deck. There were low groans and moans. But no one made a loud noise. Every midshipman knew that matters would be worse, if the captain heard the fight.

Dorgan's friends soon had enough. They fell back out of reach of Dave and John's flying fists. The midshipmen who had not been in the fight awakened. They crowded around. John warned them to stay out of the fight.

"This is between Dorgan and me," he said. "Dorgan tried to jump me. I jumped him instead."

"You dirty Scotchman," growled Dorgan. "Let me go, or I'll kill you when I get free!" He tried to kick John Paul.

John Paul fell on the kicking legs with a rope. Dorgan struggled, but John Paul looped the rope about him. Soon the large body was lashed and knotted to the deck.

"Helpless as a dead fish," Midshipman James laughed softly.

"I'll get you, too, James," snarled Dorgan.

"When I get through, you won't want to get anyone." said John Paul. He stuffed a handkerchief into Dorgan's mouth. He tied the corners of it at the back of Dorgan's neck. "When you are ready to say you are sorry, hit your head on the deck."

"You'll have to take an oath that you will never again bully anyone," John continued. "You'll have to promise us that you will never again bait a sailor. And you will also promise to act like an officer and a gentleman."

Dorgan tried to growl through the handkerchief. But he did not strike his head on the deck.

"I don't think he will promise us," said James.

Dorgan tried to move his hands. He twisted his neck. He tried to turn over. But he could find no position that was comfortable.

Two bells struck to tell that it was one o'clock. The midshipmen waited in the dark quarters. Three bells marked the half hour. Outside, a light breeze stirred the surface of the sea. The midshipmen heard the water lapping against the wooden planks of the *Sphinx*.

Four bells struck. Sweat ran from Dorgan's body. It made a wet spot on the deck.

"Oh, come on, Dorgan, say you are sorry," a friend suggested. "We don't want to sit here in the dark all night."

An angry growl came from Dorgan.

"You might as well give in first as last," another midshipman said. "Paul licked you in a fair fight."

"He's right, too," James added. "You have been a bully, and you know it."

Six bells sounded through the ship. It was three o'clock in the morning. Dorgan suddenly bumped his head on the deck. John Paul took off the handkerchief.

"Get me out of this!" coughed Dorgan. "It's killing me!"

"The first thing is to say you are sorry." John Paul's voice was low but firm.

"I am sorry."

"For being a rotter. Say it," John Paul ordered.

"I am sorry for being a rotter."

"Now, you know what else to say."

Dorgan's spirit was broken. Slowly, he whispered his promises.

John Paul took off the ropes. "We won't say one word about this to anyone," he said. "The seamen are not to know what happened to Dorgan, unless he starts bullying again. Do you all understand? We want it, word of honor."

One by one, each midshipman gave his word of honor not to tell.

"Now, Dorgan," said John Paul, "we can be friends." He stuck out his hand. Slowly, the midshipman reached out and took it.

John Paul had no more trouble with Dorgan. The big fellow was as quiet as a lamb. He watched John with wonder and respect in his eyes.

A new spirit began to appear on the *Sphinx*. The midshipmen practiced often with the small brass cannon. The first lieutenant proved an able teacher. The midshipmen cut in half their time for handling the guns.

John Paul did well at sword practice. His long steady arm was well suited for handling the blade. He earned the lieutenant's praise.

In the rigging none could keep up with John Paul. The midshipmen spent hours practicing among the masts and sails. It was a sailor's game of "follow-the-leader." John Paul led them all. He raced among the sails, swift as a sea bird.

"What has come over the midshipmen?" the captain asked the first lieutenant one day. "They have more life than a herd of young seals."

"Midshipman Paul is behind it, sir," the lieutenant replied. "The others have caught his spirit. He would make a good officer."

"What kind of family does he have?"

"He is a Scotch gardener's son."

"Too bad. He doesn't have a chance," growled the captain.

John Paul was learning the work of an officer. To make certain that he would pass his examinations he studied hard.

A year and a month went by. Once more the *Sphinx* was anchored in Plymouth harbor. The great day of the examinations came. A group of officers came aboard to give the examination. There was a fever of worry among the midshipmen. But

John Paul had no fear. He knew that he had learned his lessons.

One by one, the midshipmen were called before the officers. Each man was questioned to test his knowledge. Each midshipman's record lay before the officers.

At last, John Paul's turn came. A captain put a question. John answered. He saw a first lieutenant nod. The captain put a second question. Again John Paul answered it. The captain asked no further questions. Instead, he took up John's record and studied it briefly. Then he waved a hand for the midshipman to fall back.

John Paul saluted and stepped back. He heard an officer whisper, "Scotch gardener's son."

John Paul was puzzled. He had studied hard. He had led the whole class of midshipmen. He could not understand why he had not been given a proper examination. Why had an officer whispered, "Scotch gardener's son?"

The results of the examinations were made known the next day. Dorgan was named a lieutenant in the King's Navy. Dorgan's uncle was a nobleman. James was also made a lieutenant. His father was a wealthy merchant. Several other midshipmen from important families were promoted. But John Paul was not given an officer's rank.

"Scotch gardener's son!" John Paul ground the words between his teeth. "I'll show them!"

John rushed to the midshipmen's quarters. Dragging out his sea bag, he began to pack. He heard a fierce young voice say, "A shame! A rotten shame!"

Glancing up, John saw Dave Bonner. The American lad had been too young to take the examination. Now his eyes flashed with anger.

"Everyone—even Dorgan—knew you were the best midshipman on the *Sphinx*," Dave cried. He was near tears as he spoke.

"Were is right," said John Paul. He dropped a shoe into his sea bag. "I'm through here. But I will see you again some day."

"When?"

"When America has a navy!"

John Paul Jones, American

JOHN PAUL was through with the British Navy. But he still felt the call of the sea.

The Scotch gardener's son found a place on a trading, or merchant ship. He was one of the less important officers, called the third mate.

John Paul spent several years on trading ships. He worked his way up from third mate to captain's rank. The first merchant ship that he commanded was the *Betsy*.

The young captain set out from England on a trading voyage. One day, he sailed the *Betsy* into a harbor on the island of Tobago. This island is in the West Indies. It lies off the northeastern coast of South America.

Tobago was visited by many ships. John Paul had been there on earlier voyages. He knew that sailors were to be found around its harbors. The

Betsy needed a few more seamen. Young Captain John Paul hired men at Tobago to fill the places.

The new sailors proved to be a rough lot. They stirred up trouble among the other members of the crew. They broke into the captain's cabin. They started a fight on the ship.

Finally, some of the men refused to obey the ship's officers. This was mutiny, a serious crime on shipboard.

The leader of the mutiny rushed at Captain Paul with a club. The captain's long arm swept out. His sword flashed. The man plunged forward swinging the club. The captain's sword ran him through. The man fell dead.

The crew drew back in fright. Captain Paul ordered the men below. They went quietly, without a backward glance.

John Paul stood alone on the deck. He stared at the bleeding body stretched at his feet. Horror filled his eyes. A cry choked in his throat. His shoulders shook.

"A terrible accident!" groaned Captain Paul. His head sank on his breast. His arms dropped.

He turned slowly, and made his way to his cabin.

"Call the first mate," Captain Paul said to the ship's boy.

"Aye, aye, sir."

The officer, second in command, soon stood before Captain Paul. The captain spoke rapidly.

"I have caused a man's death. But I did not intend to kill him. He led a mutiny. I drew my sword to keep order. He plunged toward me swinging a club. I caught him on the point of my sword."

"But if it was mutiny, you had the right to kill him, sir. That is the law of the sea."

"I swear upon my honor, I had no thought of killing the man. But I must report the matter at once."

"Do you mean that you are giving yourself up?" The mate looked in wonder at the captain.

"I know the justice of the peace in Tobago. I shall explain what happened. If he wishes to hold me, I shall be in his power."

"Is it wise for you to do this?"

"The man's death was an accident. I hope that

the justice will believe me. But if there is the
least shadow of doubt, I want a trial. Above
everything else, I prize my good name. I want
it cleared."

Captain Paul turned to the table. He gathered
up certain papers. With these in hand, he faced
the mate again. "I leave you in command of the
ship until I return."

"Aye, aye, sir."

Captain John Paul hurried down the gangplank. He made his way into the town. He found
the justice of the peace, and told his story.

The justice liked the captain's spirit. But he
also understood the ways of Tobago. He knew
that it was a seaman's island. He thought that
the people would take the part of the ship's
crew. He feared that they might not believe the
word of a ship's captain.

The justice leaned back in his chair. He looked
straight into the gray-black eyes under John
Paul's level brows. "Captain Paul," he said, "I
believe you when you say that the man's death
was an accident."

John Paul gave a sigh of relief. For the first time, he leaned back in his chair.

The justice continued. "But if you have a trial here, men of Tobago will decide the case. A jury of Tobago seamen won't believe your story. You should leave the island at once."

"Run away! Never! I want my name cleared."

"I understand your feelings, Captain. But you are facing hard facts. A man has died tonight at your hand. You say it was an accident. I accept your word that it was. But members of the crew may swear that the man was murdered. What can a jury do, except find you guilty?"

John Paul sat for long minutes. His head was bowed in his hands. The justice waited quietly.

At last the captain looked up. "I've always hated cruel officers," he said. "I wanted my seamen to do their work because they liked their jobs. I've never wanted them to be afraid of a whip. Can't I expect fair treatment in court?"

The justice did not try to answer. Instead, he asked, "Have you any friends on Tobago?"

"Yes, I have several friends here."

"Then I suggest that we send for them. Let us see what their advice is."

A man was sent to bring the friends named by John Paul. They soon appeared. When they heard the captain's story, they shook their heads.

"You must get away," one man said.

"Without an hour's delay!" another added. "I'll secure a horse for you at once. You can ride across the island and take a ship from there." The man left the room.

A third friend said, "This island is full of seamen. Many have been badly treated by cruel captains. On a jury, such men would find it hard to decide fairly. They might try to get even with you for the wrongs they had suffered."

"I will not run away," said Captain Paul. "I did not mean to kill the man. It was an accident."

"You haven't a chance to prove it," a friend replied.

"But I must prove it," Captain Paul cried. "I must clear my name."

The justice shook his head. "I am sure you should leave, Captain Paul. Later, you can come back. When this affair has blown over, maybe you can secure a fair trial."

"Where shall I go? What shall I do?" John Paul cried, walking up and down the room.

"Go to America, and stay there," the justice said. "Change your name! Do anything, but get away from here."

"To America," John Paul whispered. "I hadn't thought of that."

"You can leave your business affairs in the hands of a man here. Write an order to him. He will sell your interest in the *Betsy* and its cargo. He can send you the money," a friend suggested.

The man who had left the room earlier returned. "I have a fast horse for you," he said to Captain Paul.

John Paul broke off his walking. He threw himself down at a desk. He seized a pen and wrote rapidly.

Pushing the paper toward the justice, he cried, "I give in. It's against my wishes, but I'll do as you suggest. I go because you say I cannot get a fair trial in Tobago."

"You have chosen wisely," the justice answered. He looked at the paper. "I see that this is an order about your property. I shall turn this over to an agent for you."

"For twenty-six years I've tried to prove myself of worth," John Paul sighed. "I've said I'd make my mark in the world. Now, my life is in ruins."

The captain buried his face in his hands. After a moment, he looked up. "Now," he said, "I must make a new beginning. My only comfort lies in the thought that I may make that new beginning in America. My brother is there. I have long dreamed of living there. So, to America I'll go."

The men were on their feet at once. They crowded about John Paul. They clasped his hand and led him to the door.

"Here is your horse," a man said.

"Ride, Paul," a friend begged. "Ride!"

The captain went out the door. The men stood watching him mount. John Paul raised his hand in salute to them.

The justice of the peace called, "Good luck and

good riding, Captain. May you enjoy the blessings of freedom in America."

John Paul made his way quietly to America. He took comfort in the thought that his brother, William, would help him. He kept this thought in mind until he reached Fredericksburg. There, he found that William was dead.

Sorrow seized John Paul. He felt that he had touched bottom. He had been disappointed. But never before had he faced a condition as bad. He had lost his position as captain of the *Betsy*. Worse, far worse, his honor was under a cloud. And as a last blow, his brother was dead.

John Paul could neither eat nor sleep. He went from place to place hardly knowing what he did. But a ray of light dawned in the blackness.

"I am in America," he told himself. "I've wanted to make America my home. I would not have chosen to come as I have. But I am here. And these are stirring days in America."

John Paul was right. The colonists were daily growing more angry at the mother country. England had laid taxes that the colonists refused to pay. The English government sent soldiers to America. Some colonies refused to furnish the soldiers with food and shelter.

In the fall of 1774, men from twelve colonies met in Philadelphia. They set out their dislike for the laws in a message to the King of England. News of the meeting of this Continental Congress thrilled John Paul.

"The colonists aren't going to back down," he told himself. "They mean to stand up for their rights as free men."

A new idea was taking shape in John Paul's mind. A new hope was pushing the sorrow from his heart. One day he put it into words.

"I will make a new beginning here in this new land. I'll make a clean break with the past. No longer am I John Paul, Scotchman. From this day on I am John Paul Jones, American."

Officer in the Continental Navy

JOHN PAUL JONES began a new way of life. He gave up the sea. He bought land near Fredericksburg on which he grew tobacco. He traded with merchants in towns along the Atlantic Coast.

Jones was successful in his new work. People looked upon him as an able man. He made friends. But he was not happy. Often, he found himself thinking of the sea. Sometimes, he could all but feel a rolling deck beneath his feet.

Business took John Paul Jones to Edenton, North Carolina. There he went to the office of a company called Hewes and Smith. This company built ships and sent them on trading voyages.

A middle-aged man rose to meet Jones. "Can I do something for you?" the man asked.

"Yes, sir. I want to buy a ship load of goods. I am John Paul Jones."

A warm smile lighted the man's face. He held out his hand. "I am Joseph Hewes. And I've heard of you, Mr. Jones. Men say you are a good trader, and a fair one. I am glad to meet you, sir."

The two men sat down to talk of business matters. After a time, Joseph Hewes gave Jones a searching look.

"You talk like a man who knows ships."

John Paul Jones' eyes shone for a moment. Then a shadow crossed his face.

"Yes, I have spent some years at sea," he said.

Joseph Hewes was watching the younger man with keen eyes. He saw the light come and go on John Paul Jones' face.

"There is need for men who know the sea," Hewes said. "You have the manner of a man born to command."

"I have served as captain of a trading ship," Jones admitted.

"Would you take a place as a ship's officer?"

John Paul Jones felt his heart leap. Joy raced through him at thought of sailing a ship. But after a moment, he shook his head.

"No, I have decided to quit the sea," he said.

Joseph Hewes continued as though he had not heard. His voice was friendly. The look on his face was kind.

"My firm sends trading ships to the West Indies. We are in great need of a captain. It would be a favor to us, if you would take the place."

John Paul Jones did not answer at once. He seemed to be searching for the right words. Joseph Hewes waited quietly.

At last the younger man spoke in a low voice. "You are more than kind, sir, to offer me the place. I am sorry that I cannot take it."

"I am sorry, too," Joseph Hewes replied. "We need a captain."

A look of pain passed over John Paul Jones' face. Quick words burst from his lips. "You'll never know, sir," he cried, "how much I want to accept your offer."

Joseph Hewes looked at Jones with puzzled eyes. "I see that something troubles you," the older man said. "Can I help you?"

John Paul Jones' heart was warmed by the older man's friendly interest. He felt that Hewes was a man whom he could trust.

"You are right," he said. "I have met trouble."

"Trouble is sometimes eased by sharing it. If you wish to talk of yours, I shall repeat no word of it." Joseph Hewes had a quiet strength that the younger man felt.

"I know you are a man of honor," John Paul Jones said. "I believe I can trust you."

"You can trust me," Joseph Hewes promised.

John Paul Jones told the story of the accident on Tobago. He told of his plan to change his name and begin a new life.

Joseph Hewes listened quietly. When the story ended, he said, "You have, indeed, had serious trouble. I understand how deep your sorrow must be. But you did right to leave Tobago and come to America."

"My only comfort has been that I am in America," Jones replied. "I have loved this land, since I first came here as a boy of thirteen."

"I agree that you cannot accept my offer,"

Hewes said. "But you can still go to sea. And you can serve America, too, at the same time."

John Paul Jones leaned forward in his chair. "What do you mean, sir?" he asked.

Joseph Hewes smiled. "I take it you would like to go to sea again," he said. "Would you be willing to give up your business to go?"

"I'd leave the business and the plantation, too!" Jones cried. "I thought I could live a new life without the sea. But I'm sick for the smell of the salt spray."

The eager voice broke off. A frown clouded Jones' face. "But what's the use to talk of it," he sighed. "I can't go back to a merchant ship."

"Could you go to sea on a ship-of-war?" Joseph Hewes' voice was almost a whisper.

"A ship-of-war! Whose?"

"America's."

The two men faced each other with searching eyes. A long silence hung between them. John Paul Jones broke it at last, with a question.

"Do you mean that the colonies are preparing to fight Britain?"

"The American colonies will not start a war. But they will defend their rights. To do so may require a navy."

"Will the Continental Congress form a navy?" Jones asked.

Joseph Hewes studied the younger man for a long moment. Then he said, "Mr. Jones, I am a member of the Continental Congress. I can promise you that the Congress will soon form a navy."

"Then you will want men for that navy?"

"Men and ships! Those we must have."

"When do you expect to get them?"

"Within the next few months. I leave soon for Philadelphia where the Congress will be meeting. There are plans to form a strong Committee on Naval Affairs."

"With your knowledge of ships, you should be a member of that committee," Jones said.

The older man bowed. "Thank you, sir. Perhaps I shall be named a member. In any case, I am watching for men and ships that we can use."

"Do you think I might be one of those men?"

"That I do!" Joseph Hewes cried. "With all my heart, I invite you to join our cause."

John Paul Jones straightened in his chair. His eyes flashed.

"I have always hated the harsh laws of the British!" he exclaimed. "America has long had my heart. She shall also have my sword! Mr. Hewes, I accept your offer."

The two men shook hands.

Joseph Hewes spoke of plans for the future. "After a navy is ordered our first task will be to get ships. That may take months. Go on with your business, until you receive a call from me. But be ready to leave on a moment's notice."

John Paul Jones nodded. "I shall put my affairs in order. When you send for me, I'll start for Philadelphia at once."

The two men completed their plans. Jones rose to leave. "There's another man who would be a help to the American Navy," he said.

"Who is that?"

"Dave Bonner. He served as a midshipman in the British Navy."

"How can I get in touch with him?" Joseph Hewes asked.

"Through Dr. Benjamin Franklin, I think," John Paul Jones replied. "Dr. Franklin got Dave the place as midshipman."

"I shall see Dr. Franklin as soon as I reach Philadelphia," Hewes said.

John Paul Jones returned to his home in Virginia. True to his promise, he set his affairs in order. He went about his business quietly. But he eagerly read the news coming from Philadelphia. He was glad when Joseph Hewes was named to the Committee on Naval Affairs.

One day, John Paul Jones answered a loud knock at his door. He found a young man standing on the doorstep. The man's clothes were wrinkled. His face was streaked with dust.

John Paul Jones stared at the man for a moment. Then he seized the man's hand. "Dave!" he exclaimed. "Dave Bonner!"

The two men fell upon each other like a pair of bear cubs. They laughed and shook hands again and again.

John Paul Jones cried, "It's wonderful to see you, Dave. But what are you doing here?"

"Joseph Hewes sent me. He needs you in Philadelphia."

"I am at his service. When do we leave?"

"As quickly as you can mount a horse," Dave Bonner answered.

John Paul Jones was soon in the saddle. He and Dave Bonner rode north. Six days later they arrived in Philadelphia. They went at once to see Joseph Hewes.

"Welcome," Hewes said, shaking hands with them. "Sit down and let us talk."

"What news do you have about a navy?" Jones asked.

"Both good news and bad," the older man replied. "The Continental Congress has ordered the purchase of merchant ships. These are to be turned into men-of-war. But to get the ships and supplies that we need is difficult."

Hewes broke off with a sigh. For a moment he sat staring out of the window. Then, he turned back to the two younger men.

"Perhaps it will be even harder to get the right officers on the ships," he said.

"But surely there are many men ready to serve America," Jones cried.

"Yes," Hewes agreed. "There are many able men, like yourself, who ask only the chance to serve. But there are other men who want only the honor of an officer's rank. They are not fitted to command our ships-of-war. But some of them have powerful friends in Congress. They may be made officers through the help of their friends."

"Congress will do well to put the good of the navy first," Dave Bonner snapped.

"Quite true," Hewes replied. "And I hope that it will. But the leading man on the Naval Affairs Committee is from New England. He wants to name all the officers from among his New England friends."

"Does that mean there is no chance for me?" Jones demanded.

"Not so fast, my young friend," Joseph Hewes replied. "I did not say that all the officers would

be from New England. I said that one man
wanted it so."

For the first time a smile lighted Hewes' face.
"In fact, I am about to teach that man a lesson,"
he chuckled. "He must learn that in America a
man cannot decide public matters in his own
interest."

"What will you do, sir?" Dave Bonner asked.

"I'll demand that our section of the country
shall have an officer. Pennsylvania will make
the same demand. We shall show our friend
that America is more than New England."

"What do you want us to do?" John Paul Jones
asked.

"I want you to go about in Philadelphia. Meet
members of Congress. Speak a word in favor of
a strong navy."

In the weeks that followed, the two men
searched ship's stores for supplies. They studied
the ships that lay in the Delaware River. They
spent hours at the inns where members of Congress lived. And they talked earnestly of the
need for a strong navy.

One day, Joseph Hewes sent for John Paul Jones. "My plan worked!" Hewes said. "We have forced the New England man to yield. New England will have the Commodore of the Fleet. He will be Captain Esek Hopkins. But Pennsylvania will have a captain. And the South will have a lieutenant."

Hewes paused. A warm smile lighted his face. John Paul Jones waited.

Once more, Joseph Hewes spoke. "I have the honor to report that one of the first lieutenants will be John Paul Jones."

For a moment, John Paul Jones could not speak. A lump rose in his throat. Finding his voice at last, he said, "Thank you, sir. I can never tell you how grateful I am."

"You don't need to tell me," Joseph Hewes laughed. "Just show me by trimming British sails."

"That I'll do right gladly," John Paul Jones promised.

"You will serve on the *Alfred*," Joseph Hewes said. "Dave Bonner will be a second lieutenant

on the same ship. It happens that the captain
of the *Alfred* cannot come aboard for some weeks.
That leaves you in command. Commodore Hopkins has ordered that you make the ship ready for
war."

Lieutenant John Paul Jones' eyes blazed. "I'll
make the *Alfred* fit for sea duty," he promised.
"I'll make it ready to fight any British ship
afloat!"

---

1. How did John win the respect of Brains Dorgan?
2. What great decision did John make?
3. John Paul Jones had certain qualities and experi-
   ences that fitted him for service in the American
   Navy. Find what these were.
4. Read aloud the paragraph in which John Paul Jones
   accepts the offer to serve in the navy. Try to read
   the lines as you think John Paul Jones would have
   said them.

The Flag Flies

THE *Alfred* lay in the Delaware River, near Philadelphia. John Paul Jones and Dave Bonner went on board. They looked over every inch of the ship.

"She is a stout vessel," Jones said. "But she is slow, much too slow."

"Can we make her fast enough for our needs?" Dave asked.

"We'll have to make her fast. Speed is necessary in the kind of work we have to do."

John Paul Jones walked the length of the main deck. His keen eyes measured the distance.

"We need guns, too," he said. "There should be at least twenty cannon on the main deck. And we'll want a supply of smaller guns for the upper deck."

"There's not a gun on board, now," Dave said.

"Finding so many guns may be a very hard job."

"Yes, it may be," John Paul Jones agreed. "But I am giving the job to you. I know, if there are guns in the colonies, you'll find them."

Dave Bonner squared his shoulders. "I'll do my best," he promised.

John Paul Jones had much to do. He was everywhere. He looked at every plank in the ship. He studied the set of the sails. He directed the work of seamen and ship's carpenters.

The work of turning the *Alfred* into a man-of-war began. The sails were trimmed. Waste rope was cut from the rigging. These, and other changes, gave the vessel more speed.

Dave Bonner hunted for guns. For days, he carried on the search. Then, one morning, he came aboard the *Alfred*. His face wore a wide smile.

"I have good news," he said to Lieutenant Jones.

"Out with it," said Jones.

"I have found twenty cannon that will shoot nine-pound cannon balls," Dave reported.

"Twenty cannon! Nine-pounders!" John Paul Jones exclaimed. "What luck! Those are exactly what we need for the main deck. Now, if we can find guns for the upper deck, we'll be fixed."

Dave Bonner's smile turned into a chuckle. "I have found them," he said. "I have ten guns for the upper deck."

John Paul Jones reached Dave in two strides. He grasped his friend's hand in both of his.

"Dave, old fellow! I knew I could count on you. I knew you'd find guns, if there were any in America. You are the best second lieutenant a ship ever had!"

"Finding guns was a small task beside yours," Dave answered. "You are the one who has worked wonders with this ship. It's no longer a slow, old tub. It's ready to skim over the waves like a swift-flying bird."

"The ship is better for the changes we've made." John Paul Jones said. "And, now we must turn to our next tasks."

"What do you want me to do?" Dave asked.

"Have the guns brought aboard. Then, find a

large supply of powder and shot for them. While you are doing that, I shall start looking for seamen."

"That will be no easy task," Dave replied. "Men do not want to serve aboard a warship."

"That is true," Jones agreed. "They can make more money on merchant ships. So, I shall have to win them to our cause."

That very day, Lieutenant Jones set out on a search for seamen. He walked along a street near the Delaware River. In front of an inn, a group of sailors stood talking. The lieutenant stopped beside the group.

"Are any of you men looking for a job?" he asked.

For a moment, no one spoke. The men stared at John Paul Jones. Then a tall sailor spoke up, "Yes, I am."

"How would you like to serve on the *Alfred?*" Jones asked.

"You mean on the ship that's being fitted out for the American Navy?" the man asked.

"That's right."

The seaman shook his head. "No, I guess I wouldn't care to do that," he said. "Pay is not good on warships. I can make more on a merchant vessel."

John Paul Jones fixed his gaze on the seaman's tanned face. "Listen, my lad," he said, "men don't fight in the American Navy to make money. They fight for liberty."

The young lieutenant's voice was stern. The seaman could find no words to answer.

"English laws are harsh now," Jones went on. "No one knows what they may be in the years to come. Do you want your children to live like slaves?"

The seaman suddenly found his voice. "No, I don't!" he roared.

"Then you had better join the fight for freedom. You had better help teach England to respect the rights of Americans."

"I never thought of it that way," the seaman said.

John Paul Jones looked straight at the man. His voice was low and rich.

"Are you willing to join our cause?" Jones asked. "Are you willing to fight for the rights of free men?"

The seaman drew himself up to his full height. He gave his answer in ringing tones.

"I'll join your crew. And I'll fight like a wild cat. I mean for my sons to be free men."

Day after day, the lieutenant continued his search for seamen. One man after another was won to the American cause. Each one gave his promise to serve on the *Alfred.*

One morning, John Paul Jones called all the seamen on deck. "Men," he said, "we are going to sea in a month or two. There, we shall face the most powerful navy in the world. We are going to learn how to meet that navy. We are going to learn how to destroy some of its proud ships."

A cheer rang out from the crew. "Hurrah! Hurrah!" the men shouted.

Lieutenant Jones lifted his hand. The men grew silent.

"To defeat the British, we must be better than they are," he continued. "British sailors work hard and obey commands. They do it because they are afraid of being whipped."

Frowns darkened the faces of the seamen. A growl ran through their midst. John Paul Jones watched them keenly for a moment. Then, he spoke again.

"I expect you to work hard and obey commands. But I believe that you can do it without being whipped. You have promised to fight for freedom. I expect to treat you as free men, and free men need no whips."

A surprised silence hung over the crew for an instant. Then, it was broken by wild cheers. The men yelled and shouted. They danced about on deck. They slapped one another on the back.

John Paul Jones watched them. A little smile touched his mouth.

When the cheers had died down, the lieutenant put a question. "Will you show me that free Americans can be counted on to work and obey orders?"

"Aye, aye, sir!" roared the sailors. Not one voice was faint.

Then, began the hardest training ever seen on a ship-of-war. Lieutenant Jones taught his men the rules of naval fighting. He drilled them in the use of guns. His orders rang out, calling the crew to further practice. Gun crew raced against gun crew, gunner against gunner.

"The men are good," John Paul Jones said to Dave Bonner. "They handle the guns like old fighters."

"Yes," Dave agreed, "but you have given them more than knowledge of guns. I have never seen men work as hard, or obey orders as quickly. Their spirit is wonderful."

"They have the spirits of free men," John Paul Jones replied. "And free men have much to gain by working hard and obeying orders."

One cold winter day, a boat put out from shore. The men in it rowed toward the *Alfred*.

Lieutenant Jones studied the boat through his glass. Then, he gave the command that called the seamen on deck.

"Take your stations to receive the Commodore of the American Fleet," he ordered.

The men jumped to their places. They formed a double row, or column, on the deck. They stood straight and stiff, their eyes to the front.

Lieutenant John Paul Jones took his place at the head of the column. Beside him stood his second lieutenant, Dave Bonner.

The rowboat reached the ship. A few minutes later Commodore Esek Hopkins came over the ship's side. The commodore was followed by a group of young officers.

Lieutenant Jones walked between the rows of men. Facing the commodore he saluted.

"Sir," he said, "the ship is yours. I am at your command."

The commodore looked at the men standing stiffly at attention. He looked at the guns, each in its proper place. His glance took in the well-scrubbed deck and the shining brass rail. His pale blue eyes glowed with pleasure.

"A good ship you have made her, Lieutenant," he said. His voice boomed through the vessel.

"Thank you, sir," John Paul Jones replied. "But I could never have done it without the help

of my men. There never were more loyal seamen on a ship."

The faces of the sailors lighted with pleasure at their lieutenant's words of praise.

A young officer who had followed the commodore aboard stepped forward. He held a package in his hand.

"The flag, sir," the officer said.

Commodore Hopkins took the package. Turning to John Paul Jones, the commodore spoke.

"Today the flag will be raised on the first American ship-of-war. Lieutenant, it shall be your honor to raise that flag."

The commodore handed the package to John Paul Jones. The lieutenant received it with trembling hands.

"Sir," he said, "this is indeed a great honor. Would you give the order for the raising?"

"I will," replied the commodore.

Lieutenant Jones walked to the flag rope. He opened the package and shook out the flag. Its silk folds gleamed in the winter sunshine. He fastened the flag to the rope.

"Raise the flag!" roared Commodore Hopkins.

The drummers beat the drums. John Paul Jones pulled the flag rope.

Up, up, went the flag. Slowly it rose, until it hung at the very top of the mainmast. Its folds caught the wind. Suddenly, the flag floated out full length in the breeze. Its proud colors gleamed high above the deck of the *Alfred*.

A low-spoken order from Dave Bonner sent the gunners to their places. A moment later, the guns boomed a salute to the first flag on an American warship.

Lieutenant John Paul Jones stood at salute. His eyes were fixed on the shining colors floating overhead. His throat choked. His heart pounded. But his racing thoughts took shape.

"A new flag! A new navy! A new freedom!"

Then John Paul Jones added a pledge to himself. "I will fight for this flag. I will serve this navy well. I will help bring freedom to America."

Gunpowder and Cannon

ONE FEBRUARY DAY in 1776, the *Alfred* sailed down the Delaware River. Behind her came four other war vessels. Commodore Esek Hopkins was taking the American fleet to sea.

Lieutenant John Paul Jones stood at the rail of the *Alfred*. Commodore Hopkins came to stand beside him.

"It's good to be putting out to sea," John Paul Jones said.

"Yes," the older officer agreed. "We'll soon sail into the Atlantic. And plenty of work is waiting for us there, too."

The commodore's broad, red face grew serious. Turning to Jones, he spoke again, "I have not yet told the plans for this voyage. But it is time that you and the other officers know them. We shall sail for the West Indies."

John Paul Jones drew a quick breath. After a moment's silence, he spoke. "I know the waters around the islands well," he said.

"Have you sailed there?" the commodore asked.

"Yes, I have made trading voyages there."

"I am glad to hear that. We may need a man who knows the islands."

Commodore Hopkins looked about him. Then he spoke again in a low voice. "We go in search of cannon and gunpowder," he said.

"Our armies badly need these supplies," Lieutenant Jones replied.

"Right you are," the commodore agreed.

John Paul Jones looked at the *Alfred's* guns. He looked at the seamen going about their duties. "I think we are ready for a fight, sir," he said.

"Perhaps we shall not need to fight," Commodore Hopkins replied. "It is reported that the powder and cannon are poorly guarded. I plan to take the British by surprise."

"On what island are these war supplies stored?"

"On New Providence. Do you know it?"

"Yes, it is one of the Bahama Islands."

"That's right," Commodore Hopkins nodded. "The supplies we want are at Fort Nassau. The fort is on the north shore of the island."

"It will be easy to sail up to the fort under cover of darkness," Jones said.

The commodore shook his head. "No," he said, "I am afraid that would not be wise. We shall need to approach the fort in the daytime. Then we can see what we are doing."

John Paul Jones stared at the commodore. "But, sir," he replied, "I thought you said we would surprise the British."

"And so we shall," the commodore chuckled. "We'll fool them all right."

The lieutenant gave the commodore a long look. Then, he slowly shook his head. "I don't know how we can surprise them in daylight, sir," he said.

"We'll make the British think our ships are merchant vessels," Hopkins explained. "We'll cover the gun ports. The fighting men on board will stay out of sight."

John Paul Jones made no reply. A silence hung

between the two men for a time. It was broken
at length by a question from the commodore.

"Don't you think my plan will work?"

"I'm sorry, sir, not to agree with you," Jones
replied. "But I don't believe the British can be
fooled that easily."

The commodore's red face grew more red. His
mouth set in stubborn lines.

"We shall see how the plan works," he replied
shortly. Turning on his heel, he walked away.

The fleet sailed out of the river into the ocean.
The ships turned south and headed for the
Bahama Islands. Day after day, the wind drove
the ships forward. The cold of winter gave way
to warm, sunny days. The gray waters of the
Atlantic became sparkling blue in the sunshine.

Lieutenant John Paul Jones stood at the rail.
He searched the waters ahead through his spyglass. Dave Bonner came to stand beside him.

"You spend a lot of time looking through that
glass," Dave laughed.

"I'm watching for New Providence," Jones replied. "We should see it before the British see us."

Dave stepped closer. In a low voice he asked, "Will the commodore's plan work?"

John Paul Jones did not reply at once. His brows were drawn together in a frown. At last he turned to his friend.

"I don't see how the plan can work," he said. "But the commodore is in command of the fleet. We have no choice but to obey his orders."

"There should be something that we can do," Dave said.

"I am doing the one thing that can be done," Jones said. Once more he put the glass to his eye. "I am watching for New Providence. The commodore shall know the minute we sight it. He may then have time, before the British see us, to order—"

Suddenly, the lieutenant broke off. He leaned forward, staring through the glass. "By George, that's it!" he cried. "Tell the commodore at once. New Providence lies ahead."

Dave rushed away to carry the news to Commodore Hopkins. In a minute the officer's voice boomed out orders.

"Cover gun ports. Armed men go below deck."

Seamen hurried to obey the orders. Lieutenant Jones stood by the rail, still watching. The ships sailed on toward Fort Nassau.

Commodore Hopkins approached Lieutenant Jones. A smile played over his broad face. "Well, Lieutenant, how do you think my plan is working?" he asked.

Before John Paul Jones could reply, a cannon roared. A puff of smoke drifted out from Fort Nassau. The commodore's red face turned purple.

"By Heaven, they are firing at us!" he shouted. "We are ruined! They will wipe us out with their cannon!"

For several minutes the commodore stormed up and down the deck. Then he turned sharply to John Paul Jones.

"Don't stand there staring through a glass," he roared. "Order sails reefed. And run up the signal flags to call all the officers here. We must make a new plan."

The officers of the fleet were soon gathered on the *Alfred*.

"Gentlemen," Commodore Hopkins said, "we must make a new plan to capture the supplies. What do you suggest?"

No one spoke. After a long silence, Hopkins said, "We could sail around the island. We might land on the south shore and march to the fort."

Again there was silence. "Have you no ideas?" Hopkins snapped. Then, turning to Jones, he said, "You know these waters. What do you think of landing on the south shore?"

John Paul Jones looked the commodore full in the face. "I do not think it could be easily done," he answered.

"Why?" demanded Hopkins.

"Because there is no place on the south shore to anchor the ships. Besides that, the men would have a long march across the island."

"Perhaps you can suggest a better plan."

John Paul Jones snatched up a scrap of paper. He began to draw a map. The other officers leaned forward to watch.

"We are here before Fort Nassau," Jones said. He marked the spot on the map.

"About four miles from here on the east coast is a smaller fort. We could capture it first. A short march would then bring the men to Fort Nassau. They could attack it from the rear."

Jones pointed out the line of march on his map. The officers studied the paper.

"Where would we anchor the ships?" an officer asked.

"There is a long narrow island off the east coast," Jones said. "We could anchor off this island. The men could cross to the fort in small boats."

"Would you have us take the ships through the passage between the two islands?" Commodore Hopkins put the question to Lieutenant Jones.

The lieutenant nodded. "That is right, sir."

"It can't be done," the commodore declared. "I know that passage. There are many rocks just beneath the water. We might wreck a ship on them."

"But there is a way among the rocks," Jones said. "Ships use the passage."

"Our men don't know the way," Hopkins said.

John Paul Jones faced the commodore. "I know the passage, sir," he said. "Place me at the cross-trees of the *Alfred*. I'll guide the fleet through."

Commodore Hopkins gave John Paul Jones a searching look. The lieutenant met his gaze steadily. At last the commodore said, "Very well, we'll try your plan. Take your place at the crosstrees." Turning to the other officers, he said, "Prepare to follow the *Alfred*. We sail at once."

John Paul Jones walked across the deck to a rope ladder. He climbed quickly up the ladder. Higher and higher he went, until he reached the top of the foremast. There, he took his place at the crosstrees.

With pounding heart, the lieutenant studied the blue waves. He strained to catch every changing shade of water. His keen eyes searched for signs of rocks.

John Paul Jones found the course that the ships must follow. Far below he saw the quartermaster. The man stood at the ship's wheel. He was ready to steer the vessel through the passage. He

waited only for the lieutenant's orders. These would tell him how to turn his wheel. The wheel was marked with thirty-two divisions, or points.

The lieutenant looked over his shoulder. The other ships had taken their places, waiting to follow the *Alfred.*

"Everything depends on me," John Paul Jones thought. He opened his lips to call the command to the quartermaster. No sound came. The words choked in his throat.

Fear seized the lieutenant, but he shook it off. "I must not fail," he told himself.

Once more he opened his lips. This time the order came, sharp and clear. "Half a point to larboard, Quartermaster."

"Half a point to larboard she is, sir." The answer came faintly up to the lieutenant.

Carefully, the quartermaster set the wheel a half point to the left. The *Alfred* moved to the left. One after another, the other ships of the fleet followed her course.

John Paul Jones held his place on the swaying crosstrees. His eyes studied the blue waters below. His commands came ringing down to the quartermaster. The ships moved safely through the passage and anchored off the smaller island.

Coming down the rope ladder, John Paul Jones faced cheering seamen. "Hurrah!" the men shouted, "Hurrah for the lieutenant!"

Dave Bonner rushed up. "It was wonderful!" he cried. "You're the only man alive who could have done it!"

The commodore came forward. "Very nice work, Lieutenant," he said stiffly.

"Thank you, sir," John Paul Jones replied.

When the commodore was gone, Dave Bonner stormed, "Nice work! My eye and Betty Martin! That's mighty small praise!"

"Never mind about the praise, Dave," Jones replied. "It's capturing cannon and gunpowder that matters. And the men are already setting out to do that. I wish I were with them. But at least I can watch." He took his place at the rail, spyglass in hand.

Small boats were loaded with armed sailors and marines. The boats crossed the narrow passage. They were protected by the guns on the ships. These sent cannon balls crashing toward the little fort.

The sailors and marines leaped ashore. They dashed up the beach and attacked the fort. Their action was so rapid that the British were taken by surprise. They surrendered after a few wild shots. In a matter of minutes the fort was in the hands of the Americans.

Darkness was coming. The officer in command gave orders. "Occupy the fort tonight. We march to Nassau at daybreak."

At daybreak, John Paul Jones was high on a mast of the *Alfred*. He turned his spyglass on the little fort. His heart leaped with joy. Marines and sailors were marching away toward Fort Nassau.

When the men were out of sight, the lieutenant returned to the deck. But he could not bring himself to go below. He stood gazing in the direction of Fort Nassau.

The sun was not far up in the sky when Jones saw a boat. It was coming toward the *Alfred*. He studied the men in the boat through his glass. He saw that one was the captain of the marines. But beside the captain was a strange man.

At that moment, Commodore Hopkins came on deck. He, too, saw the boat approaching the *Alfred.* "What's the meaning of this?" he roared.

"I don't know, sir," the lieutenant replied. "But the stranger has a manner of importance."

The boat drew alongside the ship. The two men came over the rail. The captain went striding across the deck to stand before Commodore Hopkins. The captain drew himself to his full height and squared his shoulders. His voice had a proud ring as he spoke to the commodore.

"I have the honor, sir, to report the capture of Fort Nassau. And I present to you the Governor of the Bahama Islands." The captain motioned toward the stranger and added, "A prisoner of war."

The commodore's face broke into a broad smile. He seized the captain's hand and shook it warmly. "Splendid! Splendid!" he praised. His great voice boomed the length of the ship.

Then, in a quieter tone, he added, "But the gunpowder and cannon! What of them?"

The captain stood even more proudly than before. "Twenty-four barrels of gunpowder and eighty-six cannon are ours, sir."

It was a day of happiness on the *Alfred.* Officers and seamen rejoiced at the success of the voyage.

Dave Bonner and John Paul Jones stood together at the rail. "What a success!" Dave exclaimed. "Powder and guns captured! The British governor a prisoner of war! This has been a great day!"

"Indeed it has," John Paul Jones replied." "Today the American Navy won its first victory."

"And you are the one who made the victory possible. You made the plan of attack. You guided the fleet through the passage."

John Paul Jones laid his hand on his friend's shoulder. "You are very kind, Dave," he said. "But it does not matter who won the victory. Only one thing matters. We now have gunpowder and cannon to fight America's battles."

Captain at Last

THE FLEET sailed back to home waters. The cannon and gunpowder were unloaded and sent to General Washington's army.

British warships were gathering along the Atlantic Coast. They were on the lookout for the American Navy. To escape them, Commodore Hopkins took his fleet into a Rhode Island harbor.

One day in May, the commodore spoke to John Paul Jones. "The navy has need for another captain," the commodore said. "You have made a good record as a lieutenant. Therefore, I am appointing you a captain. You will take command of the *Providence*."

John Paul Jones' heart leaped. But he stood very straight and stiff. "Thank you, sir," he said. "I shall try to be worthy of the command."

"Your work will be to guard ships carrying

soldiers and supplies," the commodore continued.
"General Washington must have more troops.
He must have food and fuel. British vessels are
waiting to capture our supply ships. It will be
your job to fool them."

"Nothing would please me more," John Paul
Jones replied. "But it may also be necessary to
out-run them. Is the *Providence* a fast ship, sir?"

"Fast enough for most purposes," Hopkins
replied. "But you may make changes in her, if
you think they are needed."

"I am glad to hear that, sir," John Paul Jones
replied. "I like a fast ship. And I also like men
on whom I can count. Would it be possible, sir,
to have Dave Bonner on the *Providence*?"

The commodore drew a list of names from his
pocket. He studied the list for a time. Then,
looking up, he said, "It can be arranged. Bonner
may serve as a lieutenant on the *Providence*."

"Thank you, sir."

"You will take command of the *Providence*
at once," Commodore Hopkins continued. "Congress will act upon your appointment later."

"What are your orders, sir?" asked Jones.

"You are to guard a troop ship sailing to New York. You will leave as soon as you can make the *Providence* ready."

Captain John Paul Jones went aboard the *Providence*. He took Dave Bonner with him. The two men looked over the ship.

"She has only twelve guns," Dave Bonner said. "And they are four-pounders."

"Yes, her guns are light," Captain Jones agreed. "We can't out-fight a large ship. So we must be able to out-run one."

"Can you make her fast enough to do that?"

John Paul Jones studied the ship carefully. "She's a trim little boat," he said. "With changes she can show her heels to any British ship."

Captain Jones ordered the changes made. Under his direction, ships' carpenters and seamen worked quickly. The *Providence* was soon ready for guard duty.

The little vessel and the troop ship slipped out of the harbor. A British man-of-war made a dash for the *Providence*.

"This is where we show them our heels," John Paul Jones chuckled.

"Full sail ahead," he ordered.

"Aye, aye, sir."

The *Providence* went bounding over the waves. The British man-of-war turned her guns on the American ship. But her shots splashed into the sea.

The *Providence* led the British vessel away from the troop ship. Then she circled and joined the troop ship again. The two sailed safely on to New York. Another group of soldiers was added to General Washington's army.

The *Providence* made several voyages guarding merchant ships. She slipped in and out of harbors on the Atlantic Coast. She delivered supplies badly needed by the army and the colonists.

British vessels sighted the lively little *Providence*. But they never caught up with her. Their shots always fell short of the mark.

"The men are enjoying this contest with the British," Dave Bonner said.

John Paul Jones smiled. "To tell you the truth, Dave, I rather enjoy it myself."

"The British must be raging mad at the way we have run away from them." Dave Bonner chuckled.

Captain Jones' face grew serious. "One of these days, we'll meet a ship that we can't out-run," he said. "Then we'll see if we are smart enough to outwit the British."

"I'll count on you to outwit the whole British Navy," Dave replied.

"Thank you, old fellow," the captain said. "There's nothing I'd like better than to play a few tricks on the British."

Captain Jones received orders to guard coal ships sailing from Boston to Philadelphia. The *Providence* and its convoy slipped safely out of Boston harbor. Off the coast of New Jersey, the lookout cried, "Sail ho!"

Captain Jones ran up the rope ladder. He put his spyglass to his eye.

"British warships!" he exclaimed. "And not one, but two!"

The captain went below. He seized the trumpet through which he gave orders to other ships.

"Keep straight ahead for Philadelphia," he ordered the ships of the convoy.

"Aye, aye, sir." The answers rolled back from one coal ship after another.

"Shorten the sails," Captain Jones ordered the seamen on the *Providence*. "We'll fall behind the convoy and play with the British a bit."

Dave Bonner came to stand beside the captain. The two men watched the British warships skimming across the water. But they also watched the distance growing between the convoy and the *Providence*.

"The convoy has a start," Dave said.

"Yes, but it needs more than a start," Captain Jones replied. "It needs time to get away. We must engage the attention of these two warships for awhile."

The captain waited until the British vessels were exactly where he wanted them. Then he began to snap orders.

"Clear decks for action!"

The gun crews sprang to their stations.

"Put on more sail!"

Men raced up the rope ladders. Sails blossomed out in the wind like great white flowers.

"Swing her around, Quartermaster! Head directly for the enemy!"

"Aye, aye, sir!"

The British ships shortened sail. They began to turn, so their guns could fire from their ports.

"Splendid! Splendid!" John Paul Jones chuckled to Dave Bonner. "They are falling into my trap. They'll lose time turning. And when they are in position, we'll offer a poor target for their broadside."

"If we keep her head on, they can't hit us," Dave agreed. "Our prow is too narrow to furnish a good target."

"That's what I'm counting on," John Paul Jones replied. To the quartermaster he called, "Keep her head on!"

"Aye, aye, sir." The quartermaster's hands were tight on the wheel. He pointed the prow of the *Providence* directly at the larger British ship.

Flame gushed from the big vessel's ports. "Whoom! Whoom! Whoom!" roared the guns. Cannon balls whistled through the air. One tore a hole in a sail of the *Providence*. The rest fell into the sea. Spouts of foam lifted from the waves.

"Swing her broadside, Quartermaster!" ordered Jones.

The *Providence* turned swiftly.

"Ready with your fire, Lieutenant."

"Aye, aye, sir."

"Then give it to them, lads!"

"Fire!" shouted Lieutenant Dave Bonner.

The six small cannon on one side of the *Providence* leaped backward. Smoke drifted over the sea. The air was sharp with burning powder. A crosstree crashed on the largest British ship.

"Hurrah! Hurrah!" the American seamen shouted.

"Hard about, Quartermaster," John Paul Jones roared. "Six more men to the rigging. Keep those sails tight."

The *Providence* turned completely about. Her great white sails dipped toward the ocean. Then

she straightened out and fled over the waves.

Behind her, a sheet of flame leaped from a British vessel. The cannon roared. But the narrow stern of the *Providence* was no better target than the prow. The enemy's shot only knocked up spouts of foam.

The British warships crowded on sail. They started a wild chase after the *Providence*. The American vessel led them on a merry run.

"How foolish!" Dave Bonner cried. "They have fallen into your trap. They are so angry that they have forgotten all about the convoy."

Captain Jones held his course until darkness fell. By that time he had out-run the British ships. He circled and sailed back to his convoy.

In the early morning light, the coal ships sailed up the Delaware River. Keeping watch over them, was the *Providence*.

At Philadelphia, the seamen streamed ashore. Every one of them was bursting to tell how his captain had outwitted two British warships. The story reached the members of the Congress. The men laughed heartily at the captain's trick.

A few days after his arrival in Philadelphia, John Paul Jones went to see Joseph Hewes. The older man seized the young captain's hand.

"I am delighted to see you," he said. "The news of your success has cheered us."

John Paul Jones bowed. "Thank you, sir. I was glad to serve America."

"We need such cheer, too," Hewes continued. "You know that Congress recently declared the independence of the colonies. But we have yet to prove that independence a fact. However, a few more men like you will make victory certain."

"You are kind, sir," Captain Jones replied. "I only hope that I shall have a part in proving America's independence."

"Indeed you are to have a part," Hewes replied. "The Continental Congress has approved your appointment as a captain. More than that, the Committee on Naval Affairs has decided to send you on a new adventure. You are to take a six-weeks cruise. You may go in whatever direction you choose. You are to use your own judgment about your action."

John Paul Jones' gray-black eyes blazed. His face glowed. But words choked in his throat. After a pause he said, "This is the greatest moment in my life, sir! I have dreamed of an independent command. But I hardly dared hope that I would receive one so soon. You have done me a great honor, sir."

"You honor us with your service," Joseph Hewes replied gently. Then, in a gayer tone, he added, "We'll expect you to play more tricks on the British."

"That I'll do right gladly," Captain Jones replied. "Nothing will give me more pleasure than laughing at the British lion."

---

1. What changes were needed to turn a merchant vessel into a man-of-war?

2. What did John Paul Jones mean when he said, "Free men need no whips"? Show that the statement is still true today.

3. Find the paragraphs which show that John Paul Jones was a good navigator.

4. How did John Paul Jones outwit the British?

Laughing at the British Lion

THE *Providence* put to sea in August, 1776.

"The men are expecting some fun on this cruise," Dave Bonner said to the captain.

John Paul Jones smiled. "We must try to give them a good show," he replied.

"We should capture some British merchant ships," Dave suggested.

"I hope we may, but I mean to do more. I mean to sting the British."

"You have already stung their pride," Dave Bonner said. "Think how those captains felt when they realized they had fallen into your trap."

The voyage was favored with fair weather. The *Providence* raced over the waves. The wind laughed in her rigging.

The lookout searched the seas.

"Sail ho!"

The lookout's cry had barely died away when Captain Jones was at his side.

"Where away?" the captain asked.

The grinning sailor pointed. Through his spyglass John Paul Jones saw five sails.

The *Providence* leaped forward. Captain Jones returned to the deck. But he kept his eyes on the approaching ships. Suddenly, the largest vessel slipped from behind the other four. The captain saw a long row of savage black ports.

"A British warship!" he exclaimed.

Dave hurried up. "A frigate!" he cried.

John Paul Jones nodded. "The *Solebay*."

"She must carry at least twenty guns." Dave's face wore a worried frown.

Captain Jones studied the frigate. Suddenly, he began to bark orders.

"Head for the enemy, Quartermaster."

"Aye, aye, sir!" the quartermaster replied. The *Providence* plunged toward the *Solebay*.

"Clear the decks for action!" Jones ordered. The gun crews rushed to their places.

"Swing her broadside, Quartermaster!"

The *Providence* turned sharply to the right.

"Ready with your fire, Lieutenant?"

"Aye, aye, sir!"

"Then let them have it!" John Paul Jones' voice rang out strong and clear.

"Fire!" Lieutenant Dave Bonner ordered.

The guns of the *Providence* spoke. Cannon balls went hissing toward the *Solebay*.

"Hard about, Quartermaster! More men to the rigging. Give her full sail!" The captain's orders boomed before the roar of the guns had died.

The *Providence* whipped about like a spinning top. Men leaped to free new sails. The little ship took to her heels and fled over the waves.

For a minute, the *Solebay* made no reply to the broadside from the *Providence*. Then, with a roar of rage, her men sprang into action.

The frigate was brought into position to return the fire. Flame leaped from ten guns. The *Solebay* sent a broadside crashing toward the enemy. But, by that time, the *Providence* was a small, dancing target. The cannon balls fell far short of her.

The *Solebay* crowded on sail and followed the *Providence*. Again and again, the frigate fired, but not a shot touched the American vessel.

The crew of the *Providence* hung over the rails watching the chase. Each time the British ship fired, the Americans roared with laughter.

"The crew is with you to a man," Dave Bonner said to Captain Jones.

"They like the way we laughed at the British lion," the captain smiled.

"You did more than laugh at him," Dave Bonner chuckled. "You twisted his tail as well."

The *Providence* swept on across the waves. The *Solebay* was lost from sight.

The next day the *Providence* came upon a British merchant ship. She was easily captured.

Captain Jones placed some of his men upon the prize ship. He ordered them to take the captured vessel to an American harbor. There, the ship and cargo would be sold. Part of the money from the sale would go to the American government. Part of the money would belong to the crew of the *Providence*.

John Paul Jones now had his ship well out in the Atlantic. He began to work his way northward. A second ship was captured. A prize crew was placed on board. The prize ship sailed for an American harbor.

The next day, a third prize was captured and started toward America.

"The prizes are all valuable," Dave Bonner said. "But we are running short of water and wood. We shall need to sail for home soon."

"Water and wood we must have. But we are not going home to get them." John Paul Jones spoke firmly.

Dave Bonner looked at his friend in surprise. "But where else can we get them?" he asked.

"In Nova Scotia. The British fishing fleet is always there in late summer. The men will be salting and drying their summer catch."

"My eye and Betty Martin!" Dave exclaimed. "Think of the boats that will be gathered there! Think of the prizes we can take!"

John Paul Jones smiled. "Think of the shock we'll give the British," he chuckled.

The *Providence* sailed northwest. One September morning, the Americans saw gray cliffs rising out of the fog.

"It should be the southern coast of Nova Scotia," the captain said.

Almost at once came the lookout's sharp cry, "Sail ho!"

John Paul Jones went up the mast. His spyglass picked up great sails to the west.

"She's a big vessel," he shouted to Dave Bonner.

"Can you make out her name?" Dave called.

The captain studied the on-coming ship through his glass. "She's the *Milford*, a British frigate," he reported after a time.

The *Milford* sailed on toward the *Providence*. Suddenly, the British vessel paused and swung to the side.

"The captain is making a foolish mistake!" John Paul Jones cried. "He's preparing to give us a broadside. And he's twice the proper distance."

Puffs of black smoke poured from the *Milford*.

"Whoom! Whoom!" came the roar of her guns. Cannon balls skipped over the water. They raised white spouts of foam. But not a ball came near the *Providence*.

Captain Jones returned to the deck. "We can well afford to play with her," he said.

The *Providence* slipped away from the *Milford*, but not too fast. The big frigate waddled heavily after her. Suddenly, the *Milford* swung about and sent another broadside at the Americans. Again the shot fell into the ocean.

"Shorten sail!" John Paul Jones ordered. To Dave Bonner, he added, "We'll let that captain think he can catch us."

The *Providence* lost speed. The *Milford* came on. But as the frigate prepared for another broadside, Captain Jones gave Dave a signal.

"Up sail!" shouted Lieutenant Bonner. Sails blossomed out and took the breeze. The *Providence* leaped forward far out of range of the *Milford's* guns.

Again and again, the British frigate tried to overtake the *Providence*. But each time the little ship skipped lightly out of her reach. The morning passed, and still the game continued.

"That foolish captain doesn't mind wasting his powder and shot," Dave said.

The afternoon wore on. Still the *Milford* chased the lively *Providence*. Still the *Milford* boomed away with shot and shell. Each burst of gunfire brought howls of laughter from the delighted crew of the *Providence*.

Toward evening, John Paul Jones said, "Dave, call the lieutenant of marines."

"Aye, aye, sir."

The marine officer arrived, gun in hand. He saluted the captain.

John Paul Jones returned the salute. Then he spoke to the crew. "Men, we have led the British a merry chase today. Maybe, we have taught them something about the American Navy. Now we'll end the game by returning the *Milford's* fire."

Turning to the marine officer, he said, "Lieutenant, take your place at the rail."

"Yes, sir."

The officer moved to the rail. At that moment, black smoke again poured from the *Milford's* ports. "Whoom! Whoom!" came the crash of her guns. Cannon balls once more kicked up spouts of white foam.

John Paul Jones' rich voice rang the length of the ship. "Give her our salute, Lieutenant!"

The marine lieutenant raised his gun. He pointed it at the great British frigate, and fired. The single, tiny American shot answered the mighty roar of British cannon.

"Hurrah! Hurrah!" the men on the *Providence* shouted. They rolled on the deck in laughter.

John Paul Jones signaled to Dave Bonner.

"Up and out all sails!" the lieutenant ordered.

Seamen sprang to the rigging. Every sail on the *Providence* spread to the wind. The slow-moving *Milford* was soon left far behind.

Three days later, the *Providence* slipped into a harbor at the northeastern end of Nova Scotia. She seized three more prize ships, and took on wood and water.

Then, on she sailed, to an island near by. The

fishing fleet lay at anchor. Three hundred fisher-men were taken by surprise. Some of the ships were destroyed. The others were captured.

"What a cruise! What prizes!" Dave cried.

"Our prizes force us to go home," Captain Jones said. "We have barely enough seamen to man the prize crews. I am sorry that we must leave. There's one more thing I want to do."

"What is that?"

"I learned from the fishermen that a hundred Americans are prisoners on an island near by. They are forced to work in mines. They are treated like slaves. I want to rescue those pris-oners. But I haven't men enough to do it."

The Americans burned the buildings where the fishermen worked. Captain Jones released the fishermen and gave them boats to return home.

The *Providence* sailed south with its fleet of prize ships. In October, Captain Jones brought every vessel safely into a Rhode Island harbor. He reported at once to Commodore Hopkins.

"The cruise is completed, sir. It required six weeks and five days."

"What success did you have?" the commander growled.

John Paul Jones drew himself up to his full height. He spoke quietly, but his voice was clear and firm.

"Eight British vessels destroyed. Eight others brought in as prizes."

A smile touched Captain Jones' lips. He added, in a lighter tone, "And the pleasure of laughing at the British lion."

---

1. Why was England called the *British lion?*
2. What did John Paul Jones do to show that he was "laughing at the British lion"?
3. Why did the Americans like to capture prize ships?

Coward and Hero

COMMODORE ESEK Hopkins heard the captain's report in dead silence. The commodore's pale blue eyes stared in amazement. His broad, red face was a picture of surprise.

Then a look of relief wiped away the surprise. He grasped the captain's hand and shook it.

"By George!" he boomed, "this is wonderful! It's beyond belief! Sixteen ships in six weeks!"

After a moment, the commodore's face grew serious. In a quieter voice, he added, "America needs such news right now. Many people believe our cause is lost."

"Much has happened while I have been at sea," Captain Jones said.

"Yes, General Washington's army has been forced to retreat from New York City. His supplies are low. There is never enough food for

135

the soldiers. Winter is coming, and his men are in rags."

"This is terrible! We must get supplies for General Washington," John Paul Jones declared.

The stout old commodore threw up his hands. "That's easier said than done, I'm afraid," he replied.

"But, sir, there are supplies to be had for the taking. The British are said to be gathering an army in Canada. They are shipping tons of food and clothing to provide for that army."

Hopkins looked at the captain through narrowed eyes. "Do you think you could capture some of those supplies?" he asked.

John Paul Jones' reply was quick and firm. "Certainly, I can capture them. I could have taken more on my last trip. I returned only because I ran out of men for prize crews."

"Captain Jones, you shall make another voyage north," Commodore Hopkins declared. "I expect you to capture supplies for General Washington's army."

John Paul Jones bowed. "I shall be delighted,

sir, to undertake the cruise. I have only one request to make."

"What is that?"

"There are a hundred American prisoners on an island near Nova Scotia. They are forced to work in the mines there. I'd like to rescue those men."

"Certainly, Captain," the commodore replied. "By all means, rescue the prisoners."

"I must get to sea quickly, if I am to do that. Within a few weeks the harbors of the island will be frozen. If they are locked with ice we can not make a landing."

"You need a larger ship than the *Providence*," Hopkins suggested.

"That is true, sir."

Commodore Hopkins threw back his shoulders. "Captain Jones," he boomed in a hearty voice, "you shall take the *Alfred*."

"Why, that is very generous of you sir," the captain said.

The commodore took a turn up and down the deck. "Oh, it's nothing, nothing at all," he said.

"My duties with Congress prevent my going to sea. I'm glad to have my ship in use."

At the mention of his duties with Congress the commodore swaggered a bit.

"I'll promise to put the *Alfred* to good use," John Paul Jones said.

"Take another ship or two, if you can find crews for them. But men are hard to find."

"I'll find crews, sir."

"I suppose you would like to take your friend Bonner as one of the officers."

"Indeed I would, sir."

"It can be arranged. And now you will want to be busy getting your ships ready."

John Paul Jones decided to take one other ship besides the *Alfred*. He chose the *Hampden* as the best for his purposes.

The captain worked like a mad man for five days. He went over every inch of the *Alfred* and the *Hampden*. He ordered supplies. He engaged the crew of the *Providence* for the new voyage. He begged and scolded other seamen until he had crews for the two ships.

Dave Bonner was his right-hand man. On the last day before sailing, the two officers paused for a moment's rest.

The captain of the *Hampden* came on board. His face wore a frightened look.

"Captain Jones," he whined, "I am afraid we may lose some of the *Hampden's* crew."

"What's wrong?"

"I overheard two seamen talking. They were planning to desert. They said they could make more money serving on a merchant ship."

"What did you do?" John Paul Jones snapped.

"Do? What did I do? Why, I told you."

"Aren't you captain of the *Hampden?*" John Paul Jones demanded.

"Yes. But you are in command of this cruise. You hired the men. Why should I do anything about it?" The captain tried to laugh. But under John Paul Jones' burning gaze the laugh died on his lips.

"Set a watch on those men. Place them under arrest at the first attempt to desert." John Paul Jones' voice had the ring of steel.

The captain returned to his own ship. There was a long silence. Then Dave Bonner spoke quietly. "I'm afraid," he said, "that you have more than the weather to worry about. That man is a mouse, or worse."

The next day, the *Alfred* and the *Hampden* set out to sea. They were not yet out of the bay when a cry rose on the *Alfred*.

"Captain! Captain!" the sailors called. "The *Hampden* has run aground!"

"Impossible!" John Paul Jones thundered. "No captain would run his ship aground in his own harbor."

"But he did!" a seaman cried, pointing to the *Hampden*.

Dave Bonner raced forward. "She's stuck fast on an island near the mouth of the bay," he reported.

John Paul Jones clenched his fists. "Delay! Delay! We should be sailing north," he groaned. But after a moment, he shouted an order.

"Put her about, Quartermaster."

"Aye, aye, sir."

The *Alfred* swung about to help the *Hampden*. When high tide came in, the men got the crippled ship afloat. But she leaked badly, and had to be taken back for repairs.

To avoid delay, the *Providence* was prepared for sea. The captain and crew of the *Hampden* were placed on board the *Providence*. But John Paul Jones sent Dave Bonner aboard the smaller vessel, also.

"At least," thought Jones, "Dave will keep her from running aground."

Seven days after the first attempt, the *Alfred* and the *Providence* put to sea. They slipped safely past British ships that were lying outside the harbor. They sailed northward toward the islands off the coast of Nova Scotia.

They ran upon a merchant ship, and captured her. Captain Jones placed a prize crew aboard with orders to sail for home.

Bad weather began to build up in the north. Gales tore at the rigging. Fog hung like a blanket about the ships. Sleet cut the faces of the seamen.

The captain of the *Providence* came aboard

the *Alfred*. He handed a paper to Captain Jones.

"What is this?" the captain asked.

"It is a letter signed by the seamen of the *Providence*."

"Why are you bringing it to me?" asked John Paul Jones.

The captain lowered his eyes. He shifted his feet. At last, he mumbled, "The men are cold and afraid. They want to go home."

John Paul Jones glared at the officer. Rage choked him at first. But when he found his voice, his words cut like the lash of a whip.

"This letter is the work of a coward. I know the men on the *Providence*. Many of them were on my last cruise. They are not cowards."

Turning on his heel, John Paul Jones strode away.

That night, a ship's officer reported to Captain Jones. "Sir," he said, "we have lost sight of the *Providence's* lights."

"Put on full sail. We must find her."

"Aye, aye, sir."

The *Alfred* swung about and started the search.

Out of the darkness came a faint call, *"Alfred,
ahoy! Help!"*

A few moments later a small boat came alongside the *Alfred*.

A man, dripping wet and shivering with cold,
came over the side.

"Dave! Dave Bonner!" Captain Jones cried.
"What has happened?"

"The captain of the *Providence* has deserted.
He ordered the ship back to America. The whining
coward!" Dave ground the words between his
teeth.

"Thank fortune you got away!" John Paul
Jones cried.

"I made them put me overboard in a boat. I'm
no deserter."

The *Alfred* fought on through rough seas. She
reached the island where the prisoners were held.
Approaching a harbor, John Paul Jones studied
it through his spyglass.

"Ice! Solid ice!" he groaned. He dropped the
glass with a sigh. But almost at once he turned
to study the coast again.

"We'll circle the island," he decided. "We'll examine the other harbors."

The captain gave the orders. The *Alfred* swung slowly around the island. John Paul Jones stood at the rail, spyglass in hand. But it was the same all the way around. Ice choked every harbor.

"It's hopeless. There's no way to make a landing." The words came slowly. They were hard for the daring captain to speak.

That night, he and Dave sat in his cabin. The captain buried his face in his hands. "This is a bitter blow," he groaned. "I hate slavery. I wanted to take those poor fellows in the mines back to freedom. And now I have failed!"

"If we had been a week earlier we would have made it," Dave said. "The captain who ran the *Hampden* on the rocks is the cause of our failure. The whining coward!"

The two men sat for a time in gloomy silence. Then John Paul Jones lifted his head and squared his shoulders. "This cruise had two purposes," he said. "I have failed to rescue the prisoners. But I can still capture supplies."

"We have already sent in one prize ship, you know," Dave said.

"And that shall be only the beginning."

John Paul Jones sprang up from his chair. He paced the length of the cabin. Turning to his friend, he cried, "Put out all sails, Dave. We'll comb the sea for prizes. We came to get help for General Washington. And, by the great horn spoon, we'll get that help!"

---

1. Find sentences which show that the captain of the *Hampden* was a coward.

2. Before landing in a new place, a naval officer is often told the facts he will need to know about the place. This is called *briefing* the officer. Pretend that you are briefing John Paul Jones about Nova Scotia. What facts will he need to know? Where can you find these facts?

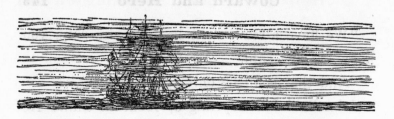

Help for General Washington

THE *Alfred* sailed down the coast of Nova Scotia. Fog hung like a blanket over the sea. On the mast, the lookout strained his eyes peering into the dim distance.

"Sail ho!" The lookout's call was low and guarded.

Dave Bonner glanced at John Paul Jones. "That's a strange tone," he said. "It's not like the lookout's usual high, clear call."

"It could mean a ship close at hand," the captain replied. He sprang for the rope ladder and raced up the mast.

"Where away?"

"Right over there," the lookout answered. "Part of a convoy."

Captain Jones gave a low whistle. "Four ships, and we are nearly upon them," he said. "Have

146

you seen the warship that is guarding them?"

"I can't be sure in this fog. But I think the warship is beyond the four vessels. There seem to be other merchant ships in the convoy, too."

"General Washington can use some of the supplies in those tubs," the captain said.

He went quickly below. "A big convoy to starboard," he told Dave Bonner. "We are going to run in and cut out the four ships nearest us."

"The fog is pretty heavy," Dave said. A worried frown wrinkled his brow.

"The fog will make a cover for our movements. Give the men their orders." John Paul Jones' voice was crisp.

"Aye, aye, sir."

The *Alfred* changed her course. Swiftly, she slipped between the ships and their protecting man-of-war. Like a ghost, she suddenly appeared out of the fog, demanding the surrender of the merchant vessels. Cut off from help, they had no choice but to surrender.

John Paul Jones wasted no time. He put prize crews aboard the merchant ships.

"Keep close to the *Alfred*," he ordered. "We'll be up and away with all possible speed."

Evening found the little fleet far from the British warship. The fog had lifted. The red and gold of a winter sunset painted sky and sea.

Dave Bonner stood watching the play of colors. John Paul Jones came to stand beside him. Looking at his friend, the captain gave a low laugh. "Feeling better, Dave?" he asked.

Dave Bonner flushed. Then he joined in the laughter. "Much better. But I did have some bad minutes this morning. Seizing convoy from under the nose of a warship is risky business. And doing it in fog is twice as dangerous."

"I knew you were worried," the captain said. "But it was a risk we had to take for General Washington."

"It was the most daring movement I've ever seen a ship make," Dave declared.

"I don't believe the captain of the British warship even saw us," Jones said.

"I'd like to have seen his face when he discovered his loss," Dave chuckled.

John Paul Jones kept the captured ships with the *Alfred*. "I don't want to risk losing them to the British," he said.

The little fleet sailed toward home waters. Once more the lookout's cry came. This time it was loud and clear.

"Sail ho!"

John Paul Jones' spyglass picked out a lone ship. "It's an armed merchant vessel," he decided.

Presently, the ship swung around so that he could count the ports on her side. "Sixteen guns!" he exclaimed.

"She may show fight," the lookout said.

"The *Alfred's* thirty guns can handle her," the captain replied.

But a look at the *Alfred's* guns was enough for the armed merchant ship. She surrendered without firing a shot.

"This is a prize worth taking!" Captain Jones exclaimed. "Supplies and an armed ship as well!"

An American crew took over the new prize. The fleet sailed on, keeping a sharp lookout for other British vessels.

One day, a large sail came into view over the rim of the world. Studying it through his glass, the captain cried, "This is the biggest one yet! And she's armed, too!"

"Do we fight?" Dave Bonner asked.

"We fight," the captain answered, "unless she surrenders without giving battle!"

Quickly, he sang out orders. "Clear decks for action! Press on all sail, Mr. Mate."

"Aye, aye, sir."

The gunners rushed to their guns. Powder boys carried up kegs of gunpowder. Seamen leaped to the rigging. Sails floated to the breeze. The *Alfred* swept toward the British ship.

"It's the *Mellish*," a seaman called, reading the ship's name on her side.

"She is riding low in the water."

"She must be heavily loaded," Dave said.

John Paul Jones watched his men preparing to fight. The two ships were drawing together. He knew that the British could see his gunners and powder boys at work. "The sight may do them good," he chuckled.

Suddenly, the *Mellish* slowed down. She started to turn. "She's going to make a run," Captain Jones said.

Instantly, he shouted orders. The *Alfred* leaped forward. She ran alongside the *Mellish*. Out of every port on the *Alfred* a black gun pointed. Through his trumpet Captain Jones called, "Surrender, or we fire!"

There was a moment's awful silence. On the *Alfred*, the gunners waited. The powder boys stood ready to light the matches. Then on the *Mellish* an officer moved to the flag rope. Slowly he hauled down the British flag.

"They've struck their colors!" an American seaman shouted. A wild cheer broke out on the *Alfred*.

Captain Jones, at once, sent a party aboard the *Mellish*. To Dave Bonner he gave a special duty.

"Find out how many men and what cargo the *Mellish* carries," he ordered.

Dave was back within the hour. "The *Mellish* carries a full company of British officers and soldiers," he reported. "They were to join the army General Burgoyne is gathering in Canada."

John Paul Jones' face lighted. "Prisoners of war! This is wonderful!" he cried. "Now, we have men to exchange for Americans held as prisoners."

"But that is not all," Dave Bonner continued. "The *Mellish* also carries gunpowder and shot."

"Splendid! Splendid!" In his excitement the captain began to pace the deck.

A broad grin broke over Dave's face. "But you have not heard all," he cried. "The *Mellish* has aboard ten thousand winter uniforms!"

John Paul Jones stopped short in his tracks. He caught his breath. "Uniforms!" he gasped.

"Uniforms," Dave repeated. "Ten thousand uniforms! And good, warm, British wool, every one of them!"

"We've done it!" shouted the captain. "We've done it! This is real help for General George Washington!"

The two men wrung each other's hands. They talked and laughed. They pranced about like schoolboys.

"Think what those uniforms will mean to an army in rags!" John Paul Jones cried.

Their excitement quickly spread to the other officers and to the crew. Shouts and laughter rang through the *Alfred*.

"We must sail for home," the captain said, when quiet returned. "We have six prizes. Winter is upon us. We are in the path of the enemy."

The ships crowded sail and made for the nearest American harbor. Late on a winter day, came the lookout's cry, "Sail ho!"

"My eye and Betty Martin!" Dave cried. "What a time to meet a ship! We haven't a crew to handle another prize."

"And we don't dare risk a fight. We might lose the *Mellish*." John Paul Jones made answer as he started aloft.

High on the mast, he peered through his glass. In the gathering dusk, he saw a big ship. She was a long way off. But she was heading swiftly for the *Alfred* and her prizes. The captain's heart missed a beat. "She can't be!" he gasped. "She can't be the *Milford*."

But she was. The ship with which the captain had played was upon him. The British lion at which he had laughed was turning to roar.

John Paul Jones was down the mast like lightning. He called his officers together, and laid out his plans. He shouted orders to the seamen. He signaled the men in charge of the prize ships.

"Put out your lights," he ordered the crews of the prize ships. "Hold your course for Boston. No matter what the *Alfred* does, hold your course. And crowd sail!"

The *Alfred* swung about until she was between the prize ships and the *Milford*. As darkness fell John Paul Jones saw the British ship coming steadily on.

"Hoist a top light," the captain ordered.

The *Alfred* held her course, the light shining from her mast. Captain Jones peered into the night. Solid blackness met his eyes. Not a light shone on the prize ships.

Toward midnight, the captain called, "Half a point to starboard, Quartermaster."

"Half a point to starboard, she is, sir."

"If the *Milford* will only follow our light," John Paul Jones said to himself.

Again the *Alfred* changed her course. The change carried her still farther from the prize ships.

The first streaks of dawn found the captain searching the sea for ships.

"Thank fortune!" he cried. "Not a prize ship in sight!" Turning, he looked in the other direction. "And the *Milford* has followed us!"

Dave Bonner joined the captain. "Do we fight her?" he asked.

"Not unless we must," Captain Jones replied. "We are in no condition to fight. We are short of men and low on supplies."

"You outwitted the *Milford* again," Dave said.

"Yes, we saved the prizes by leading the *Milford* on another wild-goose chase. Now we'll see if we can out-run her."

At that moment, the *Milford's* guns roared. A blast of cannon balls scattered over the sea. Spouts of white foam rose from the waves.

"We'll give them one round," John Paul Jones

ordered. "Then we'll crowd sail and be away from here."

Officers and men jumped to obey orders. The guns of the *Alfred* sent a parting shot. The white sails blossomed in the winter wind. The American ship set her course for Boston and swept across the waves.

On a December day, the *Alfred* dropped anchor in Boston Harbor. John Paul Jones' eyes searched the water front.

"Thank fortune!" he cried. "There are the prize ships. There is the *Mellish* with ten thousand uniforms. There is the help I promised for General Washington."

Racing in the Ranger

THE SUPPLIES brought home by John Paul Jones reached the army. On Christmas night, 1776, General Washington took his men across the Delaware River. They marched through sleet and snow to capture the enemy at Trenton, New Jersey.

News of the victory spread through the colonies. Hearing it, Captain Jones cried, "This may be the battle that saves our cause."

"And you are the one who saved the army," Dave Bonner replied.

The captain shook his head. "You praise me too highly, Dave. All I did was seize supplies."

Dave stuck to his point. "Without supplies the army could not win battles."

John Paul Jones had done a great service for America. But he received no reward. Instead

157

the command of the *Alfred* was taken from him. Congress gave seventeen other men higher ranks than his.

The captain did not accept the situation in silence. He went to Philadelphia. He protested the way he had been treated. But even more, he begged for a ship and a chance to go to sea.

Joseph Hewes had been forced by illness to leave Congress. But John Paul Jones talked to another member. "It's well known that Burgoyne has an army in Canada," Jones said. "There are reports that he will march south during the coming summer. I want nothing for myself. But I do want a chance to serve America."

The member of Congress nodded. "I believe you," he said. "I shall do all I can to help you. Where would you like to go?"

"I'd like to carry the war to English waters," the captain replied. "Then Britain would have to call ships back to guard her shores. That would weaken Burgoyne's supply line. It would also make it easier for our ships to bring in supplies."

"A splendid plan!" the member of Congress

replied. "I think we can find a ship for you."

The man paused. He glanced keenly at the young captain. Then he added, "I am sorry about the treatment you received. It was unfair. But Congress has nothing against you. Certain members just used their positions to do favors for their friends."

"We'll never make a real navy with such officers," John Paul Jones declared.

"I agree with you. And I'm not sure we shall win a war with them either."

"An officer in the navy should be both a gentleman and a seaman." John Paul Jones spoke in a quiet, sure voice.

The member of Congress tried to get a ship for Captain Jones. He made several attempts. Each time something went wrong.

Then on June 14, 1777, Congress took action on two important matters. It placed John Paul Jones in command of the *Ranger*. And it decided upon a new flag for America. The flag had thirteen stripes and thirteen stars.

America hoped to get help from France.

Benjamin Franklin and two other Americans were sent to Paris to ask for aid. They were known as American commissioners. They found the French government friendly. But France was not yet ready to give more than secret aid.

Congress ordered Captain Jones to sail to France. There, Franklin would help him get a second ship. Two vessels cruising in English waters could do more harm than one.

The *Ranger* had just been built in a New Hampshire shipyard. Captain Jones went at once to see her. He looked the ship over carefully.

"She's not fast enough for my purposes," he said. "We'll need to make some changes in her."

The ship builder's face turned fiery red. He swelled up like a turkey gobbler. "I'll have you understand that I know how to build a ship," he snapped.

John Paul Jones looked at the man. He said, "I know what this ship has to do. I am the one who must decide about her speed."

"No upstart is going to tell me how to build a ship!" The man roared at John Paul Jones.

The captain seemed not to have heard. "I want the work finished by fall," he said.

All summer, the carpenters hammered and sawed. The ship builder raged. But the changes were made as John Paul Jones ordered.

One victory the ship builder did win, however. He demanded the right to name the officers who served under Jones. Congress yielded to his demand.

Captain Jones reported this fact to Dave Bonner.

"I wanted you to be my first lieutenant," he said. "But the ship builder is going to appoint his brother-in-law."

"Never mind about my rank. Just let me serve with you," Dave begged.

"You will be on the *Ranger*," the captain promised.

"Who is this man that is to be first lieutenant?" Dave asked.

"His name is Thomas Simpson. And he has never set foot on a warship."

October found the *Ranger* making ready to

leave. Officers and crew came aboard. Supplies for the voyage were packed. The captain received his orders from the Naval Affairs Committee.

On the first day of November, the ship was ready to lift anchor. A man suddenly raced down to the water front. He waved a paper.

"A message for Captain Jones!" he shouted.

"Bring the messenger on board," John Paul Jones ordered.

The man soon appeared on deck. He handed the paper to Captain Jones. The captain broke the seal and read the message.

Turning to Lieutenant Simpson, the captain said, "Call all hands on deck."

"Aye, aye, sir."

The signal was quickly given. Officers and crew came pouring on deck. Every face held a question. But the captain said never a word until every one had arrived.

Then, facing the company, John Paul Jones spoke. "There has been a great battle. General Burgoyne led his army into New York. At Saratoga, he met an American army."

The captain paused and glanced about. Every eye was on him. No one moved. The only sound was a gasp as a seaman drew a quick breath.

A smile broke across the captain's face. Quickly, he added, "And, at Saratoga, General Burgoyne surrendered."

The silence held for a second. Then the meaning of the captain's words became clear to the seamen.

"Hurrah! Hurrah! Hurrah!" The men stamped their feet. They sprang into the air. They rolled on the deck.

When the noise had quieted a bit, John Paul Jones spoke again. "Congress has ordered us to carry the news to the American commissioners in France. This victory may bring France into the war."

Again the men shouted. The captain raised his hand for silence. Once more he spoke. "We must sail with all possible speed. The northern route is the shortest. But it will be stormy at this season. That means a hard trip. Can I count on you, men?"

"Aye, aye, sir!" The shout of the seamen was a great swelling song of joy.

"Up anchors!" John Paul Jones gave the cry from deep in his chest.

The men flew to their duties. The anchor chain grumbled and scraped.

"Set half sail, Mr. Mate."

"Aye, aye, sir!" The white sails filled.

"Raise the flag."

America's new flag rose whipping up the mast. Looking at it, Captain Jones thought of the victory at Saratoga.

"A new flag soon to fly over a free land!" he whispered to himself.

The *Ranger* raced the storms across the Atlantic. The captain drove the ship dead into the wind. He crowded on sail until the great masts bent.

The men worked eight hours and were off four. But the captain seemed never to sleep. He was everywhere. He directed every move of the ship.

A sleet storm lashed the deck. Ice covered the

ship. The sails blew out in great white puffs. The masts creaked and groaned with the weight of the full-blown sails. Men struggled, half-frozen, with the ropes.

"Here, drink this while it's hot." John Paul Jones thrust a cup of steaming liquid into a sailor's hands.

In his surprise, the man all but dropped the cup. "Why, sir," he gasped, "you shouldn't be waiting on me."

"It's an honor to serve a man who shows your courage. You are fighting for America by sticking to a tough job."

The captain moved on to the next seaman. He handed out another hot drink. He spoke another word of praise for work well done.

One day, a sudden and strong wind struck. The ship rolled from side to side.

"She's going to turn over," a hard-faced sea-man screamed.

Quick as lightning, John Paul Jones seized a hatchet. He struck a mighty blow. A sail dropped. The ship righted herself.

A loud sigh of relief broke from the seaman. "The captain can handle a ship!" he cried.

So it went, all the way across the Atlantic. The men fought sea and wind. They worked like slaves. But their spirits were the spirits of free men. They obeyed orders. They made no complaints. And always they sang.

Their song sprang from the joy in their hearts. But it was given words by the youngest midshipman on board. Quickly the men caught up the words and the tune. From one end of the ship to the other rang the "Song of the *Ranger.*"

So now we had him hard and fast,
Burgoyne laid down his arms at last,
And that is why we brave the blast,
To carry the news to London!

Heigh-ho! Carry the news!
Go! Carry the news to London.
Tell old King George he's undone!
Heigh-ho! Car-r-r-y the news!

And carry the news to London they did. Not far off the French coast, John Paul Jones sighted a Dutch ship. He put the *Ranger* alongside. Seizing his trumpet, he spoke to the Dutch captain.

"General Burgoyne surrendered his army at Saratoga," he shouted. "A great victory for the Americans!"

The Dutch captain had no love for England, an old sea rival. "Good! Good!" he shouted, slapping his leg.

John Paul Jones once more spoke into his trumpet. "I'll be thankful, if you will repeat the news to any British captain you may meet."

The Dutchman roared with laughter. He nodded and waved his hands.

"That should make certain that we have carried the news to London," the captain said. "And now we must carry it to Benjamin Franklin in Paris!"

---

1. What new plan for carrying on the war did John Paul Jones suggest?

2. What qualities did John Paul Jones believe that an officer in the navy should have?

3. A song sung by sailors while working is called a *chantey*. Find and sing some chanteys.

The Lost Command

ON A GRAY December morning, the *Ranger* dropped anchor in a French harbor. The captain stood at the rail as the ship slipped into place. Beside him was Dave Bonner.

"I suppose you will leave at once for Paris," Dave said.

"By the first coach," John Paul Jones answered. "I must carry the news to Dr. Franklin."

Dave smiled. "I have pleasant memories of Dr. Franklin," he said. "You know, he had me appointed a midshipman in the British Navy. I have never forgotten his kindness."

"He is one of America's great men," the captain replied. "I have never met him, but I have long admired him."

"The reports are that he is much liked by the French people."

"Yes, I have heard those reports," Captain Jones agreed. "Men of learning repeat his wise sayings. Women of fashion have their gloves dyed a new shade called 'Franklin'."

Dave Bonner laughed. "It's something new when an American sets the fashion in France," he said.

John Paul Jones went at once to Paris. He stepped from his coach at the house where Benjamin Franklin lived. A servant showed him into a long room. A blaze glowed in a fireplace at the far end of the room. An old man sat in a deep armchair before the fire.

Walking toward him, the captain saw that the man's flowing hair was gray. The eyes that looked out from behind steel-rimmed spectacles held a merry twinkle.

Benjamin Franklin rose from his chair. "Welcome," he said, giving the captain a warm handclasp.

When the two men were seated, Franklin said, "I am glad you are here. I had a letter from the Committee on Naval Affairs. The members told me of the service you have given America."

"I am eager to talk over my plans with you," the captain said. "But first I must give you an important message."

"I shall be glad to hear the message."

"I bring, sir, the news that Burgoyne's army surrendered at Saratoga."

Benjamin Franklin's face lighted. He leaned forward and laid a hand lightly on Jones' arm for a minute.

"That is a welcome message, indeed, Captain," he said. "I can guess how you must have sailed your ship to bring it. I hope you are not going to be too disappointed. But the fact is, the glad news reached me this morning. It was brought by a Boston merchant who traveled on a fast French ship."

John Paul Jones' face fell. He gazed into the fire without speaking, for a time. Then he looked up to say, "Of course I am disappointed. I wanted to be the first to tell you. But after all, it's the news that is important, not the messenger."

"You are right, Captain. And the news is **very** important."

"This victory should make the French more willing to help us," Captain Jones said.

"It is what we need," Franklin replied. He leaned forward, and spoke in a guarded voice. "Before long we shall receive more than secret help. Of that I am sure."

"Is there a chance that France may go to war against Britain?" Jones asked.

"Better than a chance. If all goes as I think, France will agree to fight with America. The French have been waiting for proof that we could win. They had such proof at Saratoga."

John Paul Jones leaned forward. "Do you think, sir, that some of the French aid may be ships?"

"I am sure of it." The older man lowered his voice almost to a whisper. "A new ship is being finished now for our use," he said.

The captain's face glowed. His eyes sparkled. "Where is the ship?" he asked.

"In Holland," Franklin answered. "She's a splendid frigate named the *Indien*."

"A frigate! How wonderful!"

Benjamin Franklin nodded. "Thirty-six guns," he said.

"She will be one of the best ships afloat," John Paul Jones replied.

Franklin went on, "You understand that the matter is yet a secret. The Dutch have allowed the ship to be built in Holland. But if the British knew it was for us, they would make trouble for the French."

"How have you been able to get it done, sir?"

"The French have given us secret help."

"Such a vessel could do great damage in English waters," the captain suggested.

"You are right," Franklin replied. "And perhaps it will. The commissioners have heard of your plan to sail there. We believe it is good."

John Paul Jones' face showed his happiness. "I am glad, sir, that you find the plan good," he said.

Benjamin Franklin looked hard at the younger man. Then he took off his spectacles and wiped them. He spent a long time polishing the glasses. John Paul Jones waited.

Looking up at last, Franklin smiled at the younger man. Then he said, "The commissioners have decided to give you the command of the *Indien*."

John Paul Jones sat bolt upright in his chair. His eyes blazed. His throat choked.

"A frigate!" he gasped. "Sir, this is more than I dared to hope. It has always been my dream to command a frigate."

"And command one you shall, if all goes well," Benjamin Franklin said.

"I would like to take the *Ranger*, too, sir. We can strike the British better with two ships than with one."

"By all means. If we had the ships, I'd give you a fleet. There's nothing I'd like better than to strike the British." Benjamin Franklin settled back in his chair with a chuckle.

"I sailed the *Ranger* hard coming over. There are repairs to be made," the captain said.

"Put your ship in order. Be prepared to cruise in English waters when the *Indien* is ready," Franklin said.

"One thing about this cruise troubles me," John Paul Jones said.

"What is that?"

"We are going out to sink English ships. We may burn some English towns along the coasts. But we shall not take many prize ships."

"I suppose the seamen would rather capture prizes," Franklin said. "They share in the returns from prizes. But a ship sunk, or a city burned, brings them no money."

"That's it exactly, sir," the captain replied. "It will be hard to keep the men content on this cruise. For I propose to go in the way of danger. We are going out to punish the British."

Benjamin Franklin did not reply at once. Chin in hand, he gazed into the fire.

At length, he looked up. "Men who go in the way of danger should have special mention," Franklin said. "The commissioners will write Congress of the service these men give. We cannot offer them prize money. But we can give them praise for their courage."

"That will be most kind of you, sir. It will help

them face danger to know that they are not over-looked," the captain replied.

The visit finished, John Paul Jones returned to his ship. He set about at once having repairs made. While the work was being done he spent some time in Paris. Through Benjamin Franklin, he met many people and made new friends.

The time for sailing drew near. John Paul Jones returned to his ship. He called his officers together. He explained the purpose of the cruise.

"We are going to destroy British ships in their home waters," he said. "We will raid towns along the coasts. We will frighten the British, and cause them to bring warships home."

"Don't you intend to capture prizes?" Lieutenant Simpson asked.

"We may take a few. But that is not our first business."

"The men will not like it," Simpson warned. "They will think it a foolish plan."

"The officers can overcome that idea, if they think it a good plan." John Paul Jones looked the lieutenant straight in the eye.

The lieutenant's eyes dropped under the sharp gaze of the captain.

A few days later, a letter arrived for John Paul Jones. "It may be word that the *Indien* is ready," he thought. He took the letter to his cabin.

Opening the letter, the captain saw that it was from Benjamin Franklin. His eyes sparkled with excitement. He began to read.

After a few lines the sparkle died. His face grew pale. "It can't be true," he gasped. "It can't be."

The captain read on to the end of the letter. He could not believe what he had seen. He read it over again.

"The English learned about the *Indien*," Franklin had written. "To save the ship from being seized the French bought it. But they dare not turn it over to us. Now it is not possible for the commissioners to give you a ship."

The letter fell from the captain's fingers. He buried his face in his hands. "The *Indien* lost to me," he groaned. "My command of a frigate gone. It is almost too much!"

John Paul Jones was deeply disappointed. Bitter thoughts raced through his mind. But it was only for a few minutes. Then he lifted his head and squared his shoulders.

Taking up Franklin's letter again, he read on. "The commissioners wish you to prepare the *Ranger* for sea. Use her in the manner you judge best for hurting the enemy."

The captain dropped the letter.

"The *Ranger* is not the ship I'd choose," he said to himself. "But the orders suit me exactly."

A little smile began to play about the captain's mouth. "I am free to go where I please," he thought. "I am to decide how the *Ranger* can best hurt the enemy."

The captain jumped to his feet. He strode back and forth, his mind already busy with plans.

"We'll strike the British in their own waters," he thought. "We'll burn Whitehaven. We'll send their ships to the bottom of the sea."

The captain gave a short laugh. Striking the table with his fist, he cried, "Oh, we'll hurt the enemy! Let there be no doubt about that!"

Singeing the King's Beard

JOHN PAUL JONES prepared the *Ranger* to sail alone against Britain. The mainmast was moved forward. Lead was poured into the hold of the ship to give her better balance. Sails and rigging were changed to give greater speed.

"What is the use of all these changes?" asked Lieutenant Simpson. "The *Ranger* was good enough."

"Not good enough now," Jones said. "We are going to burn the beard of the King of England. Powerful ships will be after us. We must be ready to out-fight and out-sail them."

When the *Ranger* put to sea she rode the waves gaily. John Paul Jones sang out an order.

"Put her before the wind, Quartermaster."

"Aye, aye, sir."

The *Ranger* shot through the water. She was a

thing alive. She lifted her prow and tossed it. She leaped like a flying fish.

A part of the French fleet lay in a bay on the coast. The white sails shone across the water. The gun ports were black in the sunlight.

From the deck of the *Ranger*, Captain Jones looked at the French vessels. Then he glanced at the flag flying from his ship's masthead. Turning to Dave Bonner, he said, "We are going to sail into the bay. We shall get a salute to the American flag from this fleet."

"It will be the first salute given to America by any nation," Dave said.

The captain nodded. "The very first," he agreed. "It will be a salute to American independence."

Turning to Lieutenant Simpson, the captain gave the order. "Prepare the guns for a salute."

"Aye, aye, sir."

Men rushed to the six-pound cannon. The lieutenant brought down his arm. The first gun flashed fire. "Boom!" The roar rolled across the waves. Thirteen times the guns boomed.

Captain Jones watched the French fleet. There

was a moment's silence. Then a puff of smoke shot from the largest French ship. "Boom!" came the first roar of the French salute. Cannon roar followed cannon roar until the guns completed the salute.

John Paul Jones listened with a proud heart. "It is done!" he cried. "The Stars and Stripes now flies with the flags of the nations!"

On a chilly April morning, the *Ranger* swung away from the French coast. She headed north toward the Irish Sea. Coming upon a British merchant ship, the *Ranger* sank her.

That evening, Lieutenant Simpson came to the captain's cabin. "Sir," said the lieutenant, "the crew has asked me to speak to you."

"Speak," John Paul Jones replied.

"The men are growling because you sank that ship. They do not like your plans for this cruise. They want to take prizes, not sink ships."

"Call the men on deck," the captain ordered.

"Aye, aye, sir." The lieutenant's words were pleasant enough. But his face wore an ugly frown.

When the seamen were all on deck, John Paul

Jones wasted no words. "We are going to sting England wherever we can," he declared. "We may take prizes, but we'll sink more ships than we capture. Real Americans do not fight for rewards but for freedom."

The captain paused. He swept the silent company with his piercing gaze. Then he added, "But your courage will not be forgotten. The commissioners have promised to tell Congress of your brave action."

The captain's words gave the men courage.

The *Ranger* sailed on into the Irish Sea. One day the lookout's cry sounded.

With his spyglass the captain picked out a large vessel. "West, north-west, Quartermaster," he called.

"Aye, aye, sir."

The *Ranger* leaped over the waves. The new ship was an enemy merchant vessel. After one look at the *Ranger's* guns, she surrendered.

Finding the cargo of value, Captain Jones placed a prize crew on board. He sent the captured vessel to France.

"Hurrah! Hurrah!" the seamen shouted when the prize set off.

The captain spoke to Dave Bonner. "Taking a prize has put the men in better spirits. Now is the time to strike at England."

John Paul Jones called his officers together. He told them his plans. "We are going to White-haven," he said. "We'll silence the guns in the fort, and burn the ships in the harbor."

"It's dangerous business," Lieutenant Simpson muttered.

"I know the harbor. I sailed from it as a boy," Captain Jones replied.

The second lieutenant spoke. "No one has made an attack on English soil in seven hundred years. Why should we think we can do it?"

John Paul Jones gave the man a long, hard look. "I shall lead the attack myself," he said. "And I shall take only those who are willing to go."

The *Ranger* moved in near the shore under cover of night. Captain Jones called all the men on deck. A pale moon cast a faint light. The dark sails billowed and strained overhead.

John Paul Jones' voice cut through the whine of the wind. "Men, we are Americans! America can be free only by the courage of brave men! I call for men to burn the ships at Whitehaven."

There was a pause. "I'm feeling sick, Captain." It was Lieutenant Simpson's voice.

The second lieutenant spoke up quickly. "And I feel a queer sickness here." The officer laid a hand on his stomach.

John Paul Jones turned to the lieutenants. "Your illness does not surprise me," he said.

The captain turned to the other men. "Are there any among you who have strong stomachs?" he asked.

"Aye, aye, sir, I have." It was the voice of the third lieutenant. He stepped forward and stood before John Paul Jones.

"And so have I," cried Dave Bonner. He took his place beside the third lieutenant.

Other men quickly joined the two, until thirty stood ready to go.

Two boats were lowered. The men took their places. The captain took charge of one boat.

The other he placed under command of the third lieutenant.

The men rowed toward shore. But rowing against the tide made slow going. Dawn was touching the sky, when the two boats ground onto the beach. The lanterns carried by the men made a feeble glow in the gray light.

John Paul Jones gave his orders. "Lieutenant, take your men to the north side of the harbor. Burn the ships there."

To the men in his own boat, the captain said, "Follow me."

He led his little party to the fort. They came to its high, stone wall. The captain spoke a few quick words. The taller men stood close against the wall. The shorter men climbed upon their shoulders and went over the wall. The tall men followed.

"Bind the guards," John Paul Jones ordered.

Not a guard was in sight. But the men found them in an inner room. They were warming their hands before the fire. The Americans seized and bound them before they could draw their guns.

"To the cannon, men," the captain shouted.

The Americans dashed to the big guns, and stuffed them full of scrap iron.

"Every cannon is spiked," Dave Bonner reported.

"Back to the shore," John Paul Jones shouted. "Burn the ships on the south side."

The men dashed back to the beach. They found the lieutenant and his party already there. Not a spark of fire was to be seen on the north side of the harbor.

"What is the meaning of this?" John Paul Jones demanded. "Why did you not burn the ships?"

"Our lantern went out. We had no way to light the fire," the lieutenant explained. "Besides we heard noises, and it is getting light. We thought we had better leave."

John Paul Jones' face went white with rage. His eyes burned like live coals. But when he spoke his voice cut like cold steel.

"No doubt the noises were your own heart-beats, Lieutenant."

Dead silence hung over the party. The men lowered their heads. John Paul Jones gazed at the men for a long minute.

"Anger won't help them," he said to himself. "I must find a way to give them courage."

In a quieter tone, the captain spoke again. "It's too late for the north side. But we'll fire the ships on the south side."

At that moment, a seaman pointed toward the town. "Look!" he shouted. "People are coming!"

The people were coming. They were rushing toward the beach. They were shouting and shaking their fists.

"Quick! We'll fire that largest ship!" John Paul Jones pointed to a vessel near by. Even as he spoke he made a dash for the ship.

He snapped orders. "Lieutenant, find a barrel of tar. Dave, have the men throw wood into the ship."

A seaman limped up. In his hand, he held an unlighted lantern. "Sir," he said, "I'm sorry, I stumbled and fell. The lantern went out. We can't start the fire."

"By the great horn spoon, we will start it!" John Paul Jones roared. "Run to the nearest house. Break in, if you must, but get a light."

"Aye, aye, sir." The man was off in a flash.

The seamen piled wood into the ship. Along the water front the crowd gathered. Women screamed and men shouted.

The seaman pushed a lighted lantern into the captain's hands. "Here, sir, here's the light," he said.

"Now for a fire!" John Paul Jones cried. Catching up a piece of sail cloth he set it afire. He dropped the flaming cloth onto the wood. There was a crackle. A blaze shot up.

From a storehouse near by came a crash. A moment later a barrel of tar rolled out. The lieutenant and his men followed. They raced toward the ship, rolling the tar barrel before them.

"Had to break down a door, sir, but we got the tar," the lieutenant reported.

"Good work, Lieutenant. Here, lads, pour the tar onto the blaze," the captain ordered.

"Steady, Lieutenant. Here, lads, pour the
lot into the blaze," the captain ordered.

The flames licked up the tar with a mighty hiss and sizzle. The fire leaped and roared. The ship became a mass of flame.

"To the boats!" John Paul Jones shouted.

With an angry growl, the crowd pushed toward the burning vessel. John Paul Jones strode forward. He whipped out a pistol. He aimed it squarely at the people.

"Back!" he ordered. "Fall back, or I'll shoot!"

The crowd paused in its forward rush. The captain moved a step nearer, his pistol still aimed.

A woman in the crowd screamed. Suddenly, the people took to their heels. They ran up the beach. Only when they reached the streets of the town, did they stop running.

John Paul Jones stood alone on the water front. Then he walked calmly toward the boats while the men waited. But instead of stepping into the boat, he turned and watched the burning ship.

The fire ran up the masts. It leaped in the rigging. It licked at the sails. The ship was a blazing sign that John Paul Jones had struck at England.

At last, the captain turned and stepped into the boat. The men bent to the oars. The boats skipped over the water.

On shore, the crowd gave a roar of rage. The people rushed to the fort.

John Paul Jones smiled when he saw their move. "They will find the guns spiked," he said.

One cannon was finally made fit to fire. A lone cannon ball whined over the waves. But it fell far short of the boats.

"Return their fire, lads," the captain laughed.

The men seized their guns and fired. The act seemed to give them new courage. They fired again and again.

The captain watched them with a thankful heart. "Now, that the deed is done, they are beginning to enjoy it," he thought.

The boats swung alongside the *Ranger*. The men went over the side.

"Set all sail!" the captain roared.

"Aye, aye, sir."

Men raced for the rigging. The sails filled in the morning breeze. The ship dipped her nose into the waves. She swung about, and headed north. Far behind, a cloud of black smoke drifted over Whitehaven.

John Paul Jones watched the cloud of smoke. A smile touched his lips. "The *Ranger* is no frigate," he said to himself. "But we have singed the King's beard."

---

1. Discuss the different ways in which a salute may be given.
2. What did John Paul Jones mean when he said, "We have singed the King's beard"?
3. Find lines which show that John Paul Jones was a daring man.
4. Let the boys in your class pretend to be seamen who helped to burn Whitehaven. Let the girls pretend to be women of the town. Discuss the burning.

A Prize Makes Harbor

THE *Ranger* sailed along the north shore of Ireland. Her gun ports were covered. She flew a British flag to fool the enemy. She came to a harbor where a British ship lay. John Paul Jones studied the vessel through his spyglass.

"What luck!" he called to Dave Bonner. "She's a man-of-war! We'll fight her!"

Dave's face was twisted with worry. "Our men are not fighters," he said. "They haven't the spirit needed in a battle."

The captain's jaw set in a hard line. "Then I'll give them the spirit they need," he declared.

"Be on your guard," Dave warned. "The men are close to mutiny." His voice dropped almost to a whisper. "They know some of the officers are with them," he added.

At that moment, Lieutenant Simpson rushed

up to the captain. His face was pale. His eyes were wide with fear. He pointed toward the harbor.

"That's a British man-of-war, sir," he cried.

"Of course, it is," snapped Captain Jones. "And right glad I am, too. I've been wanting a fight in English waters."

"We should get away from here," the lieutenant groaned. "We want to capture prizes, not to fight warships."

John Paul Jones gave the lieutenant a long, hard look. "We stay," he said, "and we fight." He laid a loaded pistol on the rail.

A small boat put out from the British warship. It came toward the *Ranger*. Captain Jones watched through the spyglass. Suddenly, he began to snap orders.

"Crew, stay out of sight. Keep the ports covered."

Seamen hid from sight. But there were black looks for the captain. "He will kill us all yet," a hard-faced sailor muttered.

"Keep the stern pointed toward that boat,"

Captain Jones ordered the quartermaster.

"Aye, aye, sir."

The little boat came nearer and nearer. John Paul Jones saw that it carried a British officer and several seamen.

The boat changed its course. Quickly, the *Ranger* swung about, keeping her stern toward the enemy. Again the boat turned, and once more the *Ranger* swung about.

The British officer brought his boat alongside the *Ranger*. He shouted, "What ship is this?"

John Paul Jones made no reply.

The boat moved closer. "I am coming aboard," the British officer cried. "I demand to know what ship this is."

A moment later, the officer came over the side. He stepped firmly on deck and drew himself to his full height. His gold buttons gleamed in the sunshine.

"Once more, I demand—."

The officer stopped dead still in the middle of a sentence. He found himself looking down a pistol barrel.

John Paul Jones smiled faintly. His hand on the gun was steady. "Sir," he said, "you are a prisoner of war."

The officer's face went purple. "Why, you, you, you—," he sputtered.

Howls of laughter broke from the *Ranger's* crew at the officer's words. Coming out of hiding, the men roared again at sight of his rage.

"Our captain played a slick trick," the hard-faced sailor laughed.

His fellow seamen nodded and cheered.

The *Ranger's* third lieutenant rushed to the captain's side. "Sir," he said, "I'm with you in this fight."

"And so am I," shouted one officer after another. Only Lieutenant Simpson remained silent.

The guns of the British warship boomed a signal.

"They want the boat to return," Dave Bonner laughed.

The warship began to move out of the harbor. She worked her way toward the *Ranger*.

"She's the *Drake*," Captain Jones reported, looking through his spyglass.

He sang out an order. The *Ranger* began to pull out toward the open sea. "We'll fight where we want to fight," the captain said.

"She's a stout vessel," Dave Bonner remarked.

"With twenty guns," the third lieutenant said, counting the *Drake's* gun ports.

In the waters between England and Ireland, the two ships drew together. The *Ranger's* ports were uncovered. Her guns were made ready for battle.

Captain Jones gave an order. A seaman hauled down the British colors from the *Ranger's* masthead.

"No need to fool them any longer," John Paul Jones said with a smile. A little later, he shouted, "Run up the American flag."

The Stars and Stripes rippled up the mast. The flag fluttered and gleamed in the late afternoon sun.

From the *Drake* came a call, "What ship is that?"

"Make an answer while we get in position," Captain Jones ordered an officer.

The officer seized a speaking trumpet. "This is the American Continental ship, *Ranger*," he shouted. "We are waiting for you and desire that you come on."

At the same time, Captain Jones was snapping orders. Sails sprang into the wind. The *Ranger* swung about squarely in front of the *Drake's* prow. The *Ranger's* guns were turned broadside on the British ship.

John Paul Jones roared an order. "Let go your guns, Lieutenant!"

"Fire," Lieutenant Simpson called.

"Boom! Boom! Boom!" The *Ranger's* guns sent a broadside at the *Drake*. Then, the ship spun about, in order to miss the *Drake's* answering fire.

John Paul Jones whipped out his sword. Waving it high above his head, he called, "Give it to them, lads!"

A storm of cannon balls again swept through the *Drake*. Men fell in their own blood. There were cries and screams.

John Paul Jones shouted an order to the marines. "Aim for the masts and rigging. Cut her sails to pieces."

A steady stream of fire poured from the guns of the marines. The *Drake's* sails were torn to ribbons. Her flag was shot away. Her masts were crippled.

"Swing her about. Keep out of the way of her broadsides," John Paul Jones ordered.

The *Drake's* guns boomed. The *Ranger* spun about like a dancing girl. She moved so swiftly that she missed most of the *Drake's* fire.

The gunners on the *Ranger* sweated and strained. Lieutenant Simpson barked orders. The guns sent a steady stream of cannon balls crashing into the *Drake*.

"Good work, lads, I'm proud of you!" John Paul Jones cried. To Lieutenant Simpson, he added, "Well done, Lieutenant."

Dave Bonner rushed past. His face was streaked with sweat and gunpowder. "You've done it!" he shouted to John Paul Jones. "You've made fighters of these men!"

For an hour, the *Ranger's* guns pounded the enemy. The *Drake's* captain dropped dead. A lieutenant fell. Bodies of officers and seamen piled up on the deck. One by one, British guns grew silent.

"Look!" Dave Bonner shouted. "She's asking to surrender! She's asking for quarter!"

One officer on the *Drake* was still alive. He lowered the ship's colors. Then, turning, he shouted through his trumpet. His words were lost in the roar of battle.

John Paul Jones' clear voice cut through the noise. "Do you give up the ship?" he called.

"Yes, sir, we do," the British officer replied.

Firing stopped. Dead silence settled over the two ships for a moment. Then John Paul Jones shouted commands. The two ships drew together. A party was sent aboard the *Drake*.

"Make her ready to sail," the captain ordered. "The British will hear of this battle. They will send ships to chase us. We must be away from here as soon as possible."

The captain called Lieutenant Simpson before

him. "You fought well, Lieutenant," he said.
"Now I put you in command of the *Drake*. You
will follow the *Ranger*. We'll take the *Drake* into
a French harbor."

At dawn the *Ranger* and the *Drake* put on sail.
They went north around Ireland and headed for
France.

"Sail ho!"

The lookout's cry sent John Paul Jones leaping
up the rope ladders. His spyglass picked out a
sail.

"It's an enemy merchant ship," he said. "We'll
take her for a prize."

The captain ordered signals put out to tell the
Drake of his plan. Then he started after the
strange sail.

"The *Drake*'s not following, sir," the second
lieutenant reported a little later.

It was true. The *Drake* was not following
the *Ranger*. Again signals were set to tell Simpson
the plan. The *Drake* sailed away.

"She's running away," Dave Bonner reported.
"Simpson is going to make off with the *Drake*."

"By the great horn spoon, he'll not run away with her!" John Paul Jones roared. To the quartermaster, he shouted, "Swing about. Give chase to the *Drake*."

Hour after hour, the captain drove the *Ranger* under full sail. The *Drake* kept well ahead for some time. But little by little, the *Ranger* drew near the other vessel.

John Paul Jones lifted his speaking trumpet to his lips. "Ahoy, Lieutenant Simpson," he shouted.

"Yes, sir," came the reply.

"You are under arrest. I am sending a boat for you. Report to the *Ranger* at once."

"I am in command of the *Drake*," Simpson replied. "I'll take her where I please."

"You are under arrest," thundered John Paul Jones. "Return to this ship at once or I'll blow the *Drake* from under you."

"Yes, sir."

The lieutenant was brought aboard the *Ranger*, and held a prisoner. The second lieutenant took command of the *Drake*.

"Set sail for France," ordered Captain Jones.

The two ships came near a French harbor at sunset. On the masthead of the *Ranger* the American flag flew. Under it were the *Drake's* colors, turned upside down. This was the sign of the British ship's defeat.

Darkness fell. A French guard boat came alongside the *Ranger*. "Who are you, and what is your prize?" came the call.

John Paul Jones' rich voice rolled through the darkness.

"The American Continental ship *Ranger* of eighteen guns. The prize is his Britannic Majesty's late ship the *Drake*, of twenty guns."

Spies and Traitors

JOHN PAUL JONES carried the news of his victory to Benjamin Franklin.

"Splendid! I am proud of you," Franklin said. "And I know you will win other victories for America."

"That I will," the captain declared. "But before I go to sea again I must settle several matters."

"What are they?"

"Lieutenant Simpson is under arrest for trying to desert. He should be given a trial. I have two hundred prisoners taken from the captured ships. The men on the *Ranger* are homesick and have not been paid."

Benjamin Franklin shook his gray head. "You do indeed have problems," he agreed, with a deep sigh.

"And I have not yet spoken of the greatest problem," the captain said.

"What is it?"

"I need a better ship."

Benjamin Franklin sighed. "Ah, if I could only help you. But I am stopped at every turn."

"I know that America has little money," Captain Jones said.

"That is true. But worse than lack of money are people who work against their own country."

John Paul Jones asked, "Do you mean that some Americans are traitors?"

"Not many, but a few," Franklin replied. "And most of them are here in Paris. Some are spies for the British."

"Spies and traitors!" John Paul Jones exclaimed. "Why, they are a greater danger than British warships!"

"Certainly, they are. You can defeat a warship. But spies and traitors are hard to catch."

The two men sat for a long time talking of the captain's problems. Franklin sounded a warning.

"We must be on guard," he said. "Homesick, unpaid seamen might listen to the spies and traitors."

"The men must be paid. They will be, if I have to use my own money to do it." John Paul Jones' voice was quiet but firm.

"Another danger is that Lieutenant Simpson may listen to the spies and traitors."

"He may already have listened to them," the captain replied. "Perhaps that explains his actions."

"It will be hard to get a trial for Simpson," Franklin said. "The spies and traitors will stop that, too."

"I suppose they will try to stop me from getting a ship." The captain sprang up and began to pace the floor.

Then, shaking his clenched fist, he shouted, "But they won't stop me! I'll get a ship! And I'll beat the British again in their own waters."

"I shall start searching for a ship. The French government may help me to find one," Franklin said.

John Paul Jones returned to the *Ranger*. He ordered repairs made on her. He had the *Drake* prepared for sea duty. He found a place to keep his prisoners. He gave the crew of the *Ranger* half their back pay. All the expense he paid out of his own pocket.

Weeks passed. France went to war against Britain. "Now, the French can help us openly," John Paul Jones thought. "There will surely be a ship for me."

Then a letter came from Benjamin Franklin. He asked the captain to come to Paris. John Paul Jones set off with high hopes.

"Perhaps Dr. Franklin has found a ship," he said to himself.

His guess proved to be partly right. Benjamin Franklin had talked to the man at the head of the French Navy. This man promised to provide a ship for Captain Jones.

"There is one problem though," Franklin said to the captain. "That homesick crew on the *Ranger* should go back to America. But there is no one to take the ship back."

Franklin paused. He looked sharply at the captain. Then he spoke again. "There is small chance of getting a trial soon for Simpson. The French do not want him here. Would you be willing to free him, and let him take the *Ranger* home?"

The captain answered at once. "Certainly, sir. If you think that is what we should do with him, I am willing."

"You have a splendid spirit, Captain. Few men would be as kind."

"Simpson has a lion's heart and a sheep's head," Jones laughed. "Perhaps in America the lion in him will rise above the sheep."

"At least, he cannot be of use to the spies and traitors here," Franklin said. "And now, you should start finding officers and crew for the new ship."

John Paul Jones set to work at once. He began his search for men by talking to those on the *Ranger*. He told them of his plans.

"I'm going to stay with you," Dave declared.

"And so am I," a seaman shouted.

Others added their voices until twenty-seven men had agreed to stay.

"With this beginning, I shall soon have both officers and crew," the captain said.

John Paul Jones found it easier to get men than a ship. Weeks turned into months. Again and again, the French promised a vessel. But still the captain had no ship.

One day, John Paul Jones was reading *Poor Richard's Almanac*. This was a book of wise sayings written by Benjamin Franklin. In it, he said, "If you would have your business done, go; if not, send."

The captain sat thinking for a long time. Then he flung down the book and sprang to his feet.

"That's the answer to my problem," he said. "I must go myself, and get a ship."

The captain searched the harbors of France. He talked to his friends. And he found a ship that could be bought.

Then John Paul Jones took a bold step. He wrote a letter to the King of France. The King had heard of the *Ranger's* victory over the *Drake*.

He liked the spirit of the daring captain. He ordered that a ship be provided for him.

John Paul Jones had his ship. He gave it a name that honored Benjamin Franklin and his book, *Poor Richard's Almanac*. When the book was printed in French, the word "poor" in the title was changed to "bon homme." These French words mean "good man." John Paul Jones named his ship the *Bon Homme Richard*.

The captain had the *Richard* made ready. Guns were hard to find. But at last he found forty-two. They were old and none too good.

"I can't depend on guns alone," the captain said to Dave Bonner. "I must train the men to be real fighters."

Captain Jones searched the water front for men. One day, he saw a huge, young chap leaning against a wall.

"Do you want to go to sea?" Jones asked.

"I do," the man replied. "And I want to fight England."

"Where are you from?"

"From the hole that the British call a prison.

I want a chance to pay them back. They treat American prisoners like animals."

"You shall have the chance," the captain said. "What is your name?"

"Dick Dale."

"What do you know about ships?"

"I was a lieutenant on an American ship when I was made a prisoner."

"You shall be a lieutenant on the *Richard*," John Paul Jones said.

The captain completed the crew. In it he had men from many nations. He set out to make them the best crew that a ship ever had.

John Paul Jones taught the men to handle the *Richard*. He taught them to fire the guns. Most important of all, he filled them with his own fighting spirit.

Plans for sailing were made with the French government. John Paul Jones was given a fleet of seven ships. The newest ship was an American vessel, the *Alliance*. Her captain was Peter Landais, a Frenchman. There were also the *Pallas*, the *Vengeance*, and three smaller ships.

Dave Bonner stood beside John Paul Jones as the fleet put to sea. "At last you have ships," Dave said.

The captain sighed. "Yes, ships, but not the command of them," he replied. "At the last minute the French government made a new plan for the cruise. The other six captains are not bound to obey me. They may do as they like when I give an order."

"My eye and Betty Martin! What a foolish plan!" Dave cried.

"Yes," the captain agreed. "It is foolish. It is the work of spies and traitors. But I shall wait no longer. Even if every ship deserts, I'll strike a blow at Britain."

The fleet sailed from France on an August day in 1779. Near Ireland it captured several prizes. Two vessels in the fleet deserted, taking the prizes with them. A few days later a third ship slipped away.

The captain of the *Alliance* came on board the *Richard*. Peter Landais stormed up to John Paul Jones. The Frenchman had a wild gleam in his eyes. His black brows were drawn into an ugly frown. He screamed and waved clenched fists.

"You are no good! You do not know how to command a ship! You will get us all killed!"

"That will do." John Paul Jones' icy voice cut short the man's wild words. "Return to your ship," he ordered. His tone was cold as steel.

Landais gave an ugly growl, but he went. Dave Bonner rushed up. "Shall we place him under arrest?" he asked. "The man is either crazy, or a traitor."

John Paul Jones gave a deep sigh. "He may be both. But we'll give him a free hand for a time. Perhaps he will lead us to other traitors."

The captain gripped the rail. His shoulders drooped. "It's almost too much," he groaned. "First Simpson, now Landais."

But after a moment, he straightened up. Throwing back his shoulders, he cried, "Spies and traitors can't stop me! I'll strike a blow for freedom in spite of them!"

"I Have Just Begun to Fight"

JOHN PAUL JONES sailed the *Richard* north. The *Pallas* and the *Vengeance* went with him. The *Alliance* answered the will of her mad captain. Sometimes she stayed with the fleet, and sometimes she sailed off alone.

In September, the little fleet rounded the north shore of Scotland. It headed down the east coast, taking prizes and frightening the Scotch.

Still sailing south, it reached a point on the English coast. This point stretched far out into the North Sea.

In the late afternoon of the twenty-third of September, the *Richard* swung around the point. The lookout's sudden cry rang through the ship.

"Sail ho! Dead ahead!"

Captain Jones dashed up the rope ladders. He peered through his spyglass. A large fleet of

215

merchant ships was coming into view. The captain saw that the ships were guarded by two armed vessels.

In a moment, Captain Jones was down the ladder and roaring orders.

"Steer dead ahead, Quartermaster! Make for the larger warship!"

"Aye, aye, sir."

"Set the drums to beat to quarters, Lieutenant."

"Aye, aye, sir."

The marine drummers started a steady beating. At the sound, officers ran to their stations. Gun crews rushed to man the guns. Boys hurried about carrying powder and shot. They filled the water tubs and scattered sand on the deck. Sailors raced up the masts to spread more sails.

John Paul Jones studied the ships through his spyglass.

"What do you make out, sir?" Dick Dale asked.

"A frigate and a smaller warship."

Dick watched the moving sails. "The merchant ships are running for the shore," he said. "Do we try to capture them?"

"No, we attack the warship." John Paul Jones' reply was quick and sure.

Then the captain added, "I can make out the names. The frigate is the *Serapis*. The smaller vessel is the *Countess of Scarborough*."

"They look like good ships," Dick said, as the British vessels drew nearer.

"The *Serapis* is a beauty. And she has fifty guns. The *Countess* seems to have twenty." The captain was still peering through his spyglass.

Putting the glass down, he added, "We must get into position for the battle."

The *Richard* swung about. But the *Serapis* was also seeking a good position for the battle. The two ships twisted and turned. Neither captain could outwit the other.

"The captain of the *Serapis* is a smart sailor," John Paul Jones said.

The sun set in red glory. Long shadows stretched across the waves. The full moon began to rise like a golden ball out of the sea.

The two ships finally came side by side. They were not more than a pistol shot apart.

A deep voice rolled across the waves. "What ship is that?"

"I can't hear what you say," Lieutenant Dick Dale called.

"What are you carrying?"

A seaman leaned over the *Richard's* rail. "Round grape and double-headed shot," he yelled.

This gay answer delighted the sailors on the *Richard*. They almost shook the ship with their laughter.

"Are you ready, Lieutenant?" called John Paul Jones.

"Every gun is ready, sir."

"Let them have it."

"Fire," ordered Lieutenant Dick Dale.

The guns of the *Richard* roared. The guns of the *Serapis* answered. The night burst into red flame. The ships rocked under the weight of shot.

Then came a mighty blast from the lower deck of the *Richard*. The ship was almost lifted from the waves.

"Something is wrong!" Dick shouted. He ran for the lower deck.

"It's those old guns," John Paul Jones groaned.

He was right. Two eighteen-pounders had burst at the first broadside. Many men of the gun crews lay dead beside their guns.

"Close the lower deck. Get the rest of the men to the main deck," roared John Paul Jones. "And keep fighting."

The *Serapis* poured another broadside into the *Richard.* At the same time, the *Countess* ran past the American ship, firing her guns.

But at that moment the *Pallas* raced into the battle. She blasted the *Countess* with her cannon and followed with a steady stream of fire. This attack kept the *Countess* away from the *Richard.*

Again came the solid crash of a broadside. The *Richard* shivered and shook. Her sand-covered deck was soaked with blood. The air sang with flying splinters struck off by cannon balls.

John Paul Jones was everywhere. He patted a sweating gunner on the back. He helped carry a wounded man below. He loaded a gun when the gunner fell. And all the time he was planning ways to win the battle.

"Dick," the captain shouted, "their metal is too heavy for us. They will hammer us to pieces."

Dick Dale wiped the sweat from his face with a powder-stained hand. "I know, sir. They have already torn great holes in the *Richard's* sides."

"We must get close to them. We must lash the two ships together. Then our men can board the *Serapis*, and fight it out on deck."

"A good plan, sir."

"Give hooks to your men. We'll move the *Richard* alongside. The men will grab the rail of the *Serapis* with their hooks."

"Aye, aye, sir."

John Paul Jones shouted orders to the quartermaster. The *Richard* moved toward the *Serapis*. But the British ship swung about. Again, the *Richard* tried to come alongside. Again, the *Serapis* escaped to fire another broadside.

Dick Dale's men stood ready with their hooks. But the British captain kept his ship out of their reach for an hour. Then the *Richard* made a quick turn, and rammed the *Serapis*.

"Now, grab her," Dick Dale shouted.

The men threw the iron hooks over the rail of the *Serapis*. The hooks held for a moment. The *Serapis* made a swift turn. The hooks slipped, scraped along the rail, and jerked off. The *Serapis* was free. She poured another broadside into the *Richard*.

Most of the big guns on the *Richard* were knocked out. But on her upper decks French marines and sailors kept up a steady fire. With small firearms they tore the rigging and sails of the *Serapis* to bits. The British ship was growing less able to escape the *Richard*.

The American vessel made a sudden turn. The *Serapis* swung to escape and rammed the *Richard*.

The captain seized a rope. He leaped onto the *Serapis*. He lashed the two ships together.

"I have her!" John Paul Jones shouted. He leaped back onto his own ship.

The *Serapis* was caught, but she was not beaten. Her gunners, firing at close range, tore the insides out of the *Richard*. Shot from her small firearms struck down dozens of French marines. Sudden fear seized the others. They started to run.

John Paul Jones snatched a gun from a dying marine. Mounting the rail, he fired at the enemy.

"Frenchmen," he shouted, "will you give way before Americans and British?"

The marines paused in their fight. Then, with a mighty cheer, they turned back to the battle.

The *Alliance* suddenly sailed into view in the moonlight. A great shout arose on the *Richard*.

"Hurrah! Hurrah!" the men cheered. "She is coming to save us."

The *Alliance* raced past and poured a broadside into the *Richard*. Americans fell dead, struck down by American bullets.

"Stop! Stop the traitor!" men yelled.

"Landais is trying to kill us," Dave Bonner groaned.

"Run up signals. Make certain Landais knows us," Captain Jones ordered.

Signal lights were hung. Moonlight flooded the two ships locked in battle. The *Alliance* drew away. Then she swept back, and poured another round of shot into the *Richard*. Eight Americans fell dead. The *Alliance* sailed off into the night.

"Fire! Fire!" The cry rang out on the *Richard's* deck. Flames licked high into the rigging. Masts were blackened. Sails went up in puffs of blaze. Men dropped their guns to beat out the fire with wet sail cloth. They splashed buckets of water on leaping flames.

Cries rose from below. Men poured up on deck. They were English prisoners taken from prize ships.

"The ship is sinking," they screamed.

It was true. Even as he dashed toward the prisoners, the captain felt the vessel settle. He whipped out his pistol.

"To the pumps," he ordered the prisoners. "Pump for your lives. I'll shoot the first man who stops."

An officer rushed up to the captain. "The ship is on fire and sinking. For heaven sake, strike the colors, sir!"

"I will sink, but I will not strike," John Paul Jones thundered.

A shot from the *Serapis* brought down the American flag. The British seamen heard the

cries on the *Richard*. They saw that the American flag was gone. Someone shouted, "They have surrendered." The words swept across the British ship.

Hearing them, the captain of the *Serapis* stepped to the rail. He raised his trumpet and shouted to Captain Jones.

"Have you struck, sir?"

John Paul Jones seized his trumpet. In a voice that roared above the noises of the battle he made his reply.

"Struck, sir? No, I have just begun to fight!"

"Then let them have it," the British captain shouted to his gunners.

Cannon balls tore holes in the *Richard*. British seamen tried to cut the ropes that bound the ships together. But the marines picked them off one by one. The ropes held.

"Arm men to go aboard the *Serapis*," Captain Jones ordered.

Pistols and sharp weapons were handed out to twenty-five men.

The captain called a midshipman. He gave the

man an order. "Do you understand the plan?" he asked.

"Aye, aye, sir." The man broke into a grin. "It may finish them, sir."

"Then let them have it quickly."

The midshipman seized a bucket of small shells called grenades. Bucket in hand, he climbed the mainmast. When he reached a crosspiece on the mast, he crept out on it. Lying on this crosspiece he was over the deck of the *Serapis*. Beneath him was an opening in the deck.

The midshipman took a grenade from the bucket. He aimed at the opening. The grenade dropped, and burst on the deck. Again the midshipman tried. Again he missed the opening. Carefully he aimed the third grenade, and let it go.

"Crash! Bang! Boom!" A mighty roar rose from the *Serapis*. The grenade had fallen into the opening. It had landed on a store of gunpowder. In bursting, it set off the powder.

Jones turned to the men waiting to go aboard the *Serapis*. "Are you ready?" he called.

"Aye, aye, sir."

"This is your time. Go in," ordered Jones.

The men leaped the rail of the *Serapis*. They charged across the deck, firing their pistols. The British sailors were not able to stop the mad rush of the Americans.

The deck of the *Serapis* was covered with dead and dying men. Her sails hung in strings. Her rigging was shot to pieces. With a groan, her mainmast gave way. It struck the deck with a thundering crash.

The captain of the *Serapis* looked at his wrecked ship. He gazed at his dead and dying men. He heard the groans of the wounded. Then he walked to the flag staff. Slowly, slowly he hauled down the British flag.

"Sir," asked Dick Dale, "may I take him prisoner?"

"You may," Captain Jones replied.

Dick Dale sprang across the rail to the deck of the *Serapis*. He walked up to the British captain.

"Sir," he said, "I have orders to bring you on board the ship alongside."

The captain followed Dick to the deck of the *Bon Homme Richard*. He bowed, and handed his sword to John Paul Jones, without a word.

The American captain took the sword and handed it to a midshipman. Turning to the British officer, he said, "Sir, you fought a good fight. I hope your country will reward you."

---

1. What is a traitor? What officers serving under John Paul Jones acted like traitors? Find lines to support your charges against each officer.

2. Compare the *Bon Homme Richard* and the *Serapis*.

3. What does John Paul Jones' statement, "I have just begun to fight," tell you about the captain?

4. John Paul Jones has been called, "the father of the American Navy." Why is this a good title for him?

Escaping a British Trap

"LIEUTENANT DALE, take command of the *Serapis*. Make her ready to sail," John Paul Jones ordered.

"Aye, aye, sir."

"We must be away before dawn. News of this battle will spread. The British will comb the seas for us."

"Indeed, they will," Dick Dale laughed. "This is a blow that will sting British pride."

"Britain has ruled the sea for two hundred years. She has chosen the time and place to fight. Tonight, America made the choice." John Paul Jones spoke quietly, but his voice had a ring of pride.

The ships were repaired enough to sail. Before dawn the fleet was under way. But it was clear that the *Richard* was badly crippled.

John Paul Jones spoke to the carpenters about

the ship. "Save her, if you can. She made a brave fight. I want to take her into harbor."

The men hammered and sawed. They pumped water out of the *Richard*, and patched holes in her. But she continued to settle lower in the waves.

In the early morning, the chief carpenter came to John Paul Jones. "I'm sorry, sir, but the *Richard* can't be saved," he said. "I've done my best, but she's going to her grave."

"It's like losing a friend who stood by you in need," the captain replied. "But if she is to sink, we must clear her."

Orders were given. The men on the *Richard* were put on the other ships. John Paul Jones went on board the *Serapis*, and took command.

The *Richard* rocked gently on the sea. Her sails were set. Her colors streamed in the sunlight. Then her prow dipped into the foam. Slowly she sank, until her stern slipped beneath the waves.

Shortly before the *Richard* sank, the *Alliance* joined the other vessels. She circled round and

round the crippled ships. But Peter Landais made
no offer to help. After the *Richard* sank, the
Alliance sailed away.

The fleet set out for Holland. When the ships
dropped anchor in a Dutch harbor, they found
the *Alliance* there. John Paul Jones placed Peter
Landais under arrest.

"The man is probably mad," the captain said
to Dave Bonner. "But he is too dangerous to be
allowed his freedom."

"He is a traitor," Dave Bonner declared. "He
is the captain of an American ship. He fired
upon Americans in battle."

Holland was not at war. Laws prevented ships
of warring nations remaining long in the shelter
of its harbors. John Paul Jones had wounded
men. He had crippled ships. He asked to stay
long enough to care for his men. He wanted time
to repair his ships.

The British threatened to make trouble for
Holland, if she allowed the captain to stay. At
the same time, the British placed forty-two warships outside the harbor. They expected to force

the captain out into the North Sea, and then capture him.

The Dutch were troubled about what to do. The British demanded that John Paul Jones be forced to leave. The captain begged for time to prepare for a voyage to France.

There was much discussion about what would be done with the *Serapis*. John Paul Jones wanted the ship for the American Navy. The British wanted to keep the Americans from getting the *Serapis*.

Weeks turned into months, while men argued about these matters. Then, one day, a man in the service of the Dutch government called upon Captain Jones.

"My government has decided what you are to do," the man said.

"What is your decision?" asked the captain.

"You are to leave the *Serapis* here. It will be sold as a prize. But you may keep the *Alliance*. Put your men on board her. Make a run for a French harbor, if you think you can make it."

"I can make it," John Paul Jones replied.

The captain prepared the *Alliance* to sail. He placed most of his men on board. He arranged to leave the other vessels of the fleet in the Dutch harbor.

All was ready. But the winds blew out of the west.

"Oh, for an east wind to blow us toward France," the captain groaned.

Day after day, he watched the wind. But always it was from the wrong direction. The British pressed their demands that Jones leave. Still there was no east wind.

Then came a December day when the wind sang in the sails. John Paul Jones came on deck.

"An east wind!" he shouted. "Up anchors! Today, we sail for France."

The *Alliance* spread her sails. The water hissed along her sides. She headed out of the harbor. Once in the North Sea, the captain gave the sailing orders.

"Swing her west-south-west, Quartermaster."

"West-south-west she is, sir."

"What are you doing?" Dave Bonner cried.

"I thought we would head for the open sea. Then we could make a run for it."

John Paul Jones chuckled. "That's what the British will expect, too," he said. "They'll be looking for us out there. So, we are going to hug the coast and sneak through the English Channel."

Dick Dale came forward. "Captain," he said, "with this course we'll soon be in sight of the English coast."

"That's right," the captain replied. "And along the English coast no one will be expecting us."

Captain Jones laughed and added, "A fighting man should always be where he is not expected, Lieutenant."

The *Alliance* kicked her heels, and raced across the North Sea. Her cannon were neatly lashed. Her sails blew white and clean in the winter breeze.

Under cover of darkness, the *Alliance* moved into the English Channel. Morning showed the south shore of England. The sails of English ships could be seen in the distance.

On the *Alliance* men scarcely spoke. Officers

walked the deck, watching the enemy sails. Seamen went about their duties with drawn faces. John Paul Jones never left his station. He stood, spyglass in hand, peering through the gray winter light.

On and on, the *Alliance* sailed, carried by a smart east wind. The distant English ships came no nearer. As the day wore on, English shores faded from view.

The *Alliance* slipped around the western tip of France. She came to anchor in a French harbor.

"Hurrah! Hurrah! Hurrah!" The men broke into wild cheers. "Hurrah for the captain!"

"You have done it again!" Dave Bonner cried. "You have outwitted the British. You have escaped their trap."

Dick Dale gave a laugh that rolled from the depths of his great chest. "Think of sailing right past forty-two men-of-war!" he roared.

The story of John Paul Jones' victory over the *Serapis* had already reached France. People cheered him when he appeared on the street.

The captain was a dashing figure in his blue uniform. His coat was faced with tan and edged in red. On his shoulders he wore a pair of heavy gold ornaments. His three-cornered hat was decorated with a bow and an edging of white ribbon. His powdered hair was arranged in rolls above his ears, in the fashion of the day.

John Paul Jones went at once to see Benjamin Franklin. The older man's face lighted with joy when he saw the captain.

"Well done, my boy! Well done!" Franklin said. "You fought with courage and daring."

"I only did my duty, sir," the captain replied.

"It was a deed that will teach Britain to respect America," Franklin declared.

"I am ready to win other victories, if I can have a ship, sir."

The smile faded from Franklin's face. "Ah, yes, that is the trouble," he sighed.

"I suppose it's the same old story," Captain Jones said.

Franklin nodded. "The very same, except that things grow worse with each passing month.

America has little money. France is full of spies and traitors."

"You feel, then, that it will be hard to find a ship for me?" the captain asked.

"Yes, it will be hard," Franklin agreed. "But I will do my best."

The months which followed proved that Franklin understood conditions in France. He tried to find a ship for John Paul Jones. The captain tried. But they were stopped at every turn. Even the *Alliance* was lost to John Paul Jones.

Peter Landais had been ordered by Benjamin Franklin to return to America. There, he was to be tried on the charges that had caused his arrest.

The mad captain got the help of a traitor. While John Paul Jones was off the *Alliance*, Landais seized her. He dumped John Paul Jones' bags on the water front. He ordered all officers loyal to John Paul Jones to go ashore. He made all the loyal seamen prisoners. Then he sailed for America.

Dick Dale and Dave Bonner went ashore with

the other loyal officers. They carried the news to Captain Jones.

"It's a shame!" Dick stormed. "That traitor has a ship, and you are without one!"

John Paul Jones gave his two friends a long look. "Losing the *Alliance* is a blow," he said. "But the loss only means that we must search still harder for another ship."

"When you find the ship, I'll be ready to serve on it," Dave Bonner declared.

"So will I, and so will the other officers who left the *Alliance*," Dick Dale promised.

"America has need of loyal officers, such as you have proved yourselves to be," the captain said. "There is much to do. At the moment, there is need to take supplies from France to General Washington."

John Paul Jones searched harder than ever for a ship. For a time it appeared that no one had a ship for him. But the captain received a favor that he did not expect. A message came to him one day from the King of France. The message asked him to come to court.

John Paul Jones presented himself at the court. The King held a beautiful sword in his hands. The blade was of the finest steel. The hilt was of gold.

The King handed the sword to John Paul Jones. He said, "This sword is given to you by France. The French people rejoiced over your victories. They laughed at your skill in outwitting forty-two men-of-war. This sword is a mark of their respect for you, Captain Jones."

John Paul Jones bowed low. He received the sword with trembling hands.

"Sir," he said, "I thank you for this gift. I accept it, but not for myself. The brave men who fought beside me have a claim to it. The men who helped me escape the forty-two British men-of-war have a claim to it. In their names, I accept this honor paid to American fighting men."

Faithful to the End

ONE DAY Benjamin Franklin sent for John Paul Jones.

"At last, I have found a ship," Franklin said. "She is a small vessel called the *Ariel*. You are to have her loaded with supplies and take her to America."

"Splendid! When do I sail?"

"As soon as the goods can be put aboard. General Washington has great need for supplies."

"I shall sail with all possible speed," the captain promised.

"I am sorry not to give you a frigate," Franklin said. "I know you would like to strike again at the British."

"I am glad to serve America in any way that I can," the captain answered.

In October, 1780, the little ship put to sea.

240

Dick Dale and Dave Bonner sailed as officers on the *Ariel.*

On the third day out, a sudden gale lashed the waves. The sky grew black as night.

"Shall we turn back?" Dave asked.

"We could not make land in this wind," the captain replied. "We'll have to fight it out."

The wind whined and shouted. It became a steady roar. All the sails were taken down. But the wind drove the ship ahead, even with the masts bare.

"We are heading for rocks!" Dick shouted.

"We are lost!" seamen screamed.

"Lower the foretop mast." The captain's voice roared above the wind.

"Aye, aye, sir."

"Stretch the life lines."

"Aye, aye, sir."

The men strung ropes back and forth across the deck. They held onto the ropes to keep from being washed overboard.

"Let out the anchor," the captain ordered.

"Aye, aye, sir."

The men let out the rope that held the anchor. But the rope was not long enough. The anchor could not reach the bottom of the ocean.

"Splice the anchor rope!" Captain Jones shouted.

"Aye, aye, sir."

The longer rope was let out. The anchor drifted through the water. Hard-faced seamen groaned.

"Splice on another rope." The captain's voice was calm.

The rope was spliced. The anchor was dropped overboard. Foot after foot, the rope went down. It was almost to the end.

"There is no more rope to splice on," Dick Dale said.

"Cut away the foremast," the captain ordered. "Use the ropes that hold the masts to splice the anchor rope."

Dick Dale groaned, "If this doesn't let the anchor reach bottom, we are lost."

Men seized axes and chopped the foremast. They spliced the rope. It stretched tight.

"She's holding!" Dick Dale shouted. "We're saved!"

For three days and three nights, the storm raged. A few feet from the *Ariel*, the black rocks frowned. But the anchor held.

The little ship limped back to France for repairs. In December, she again set sail for America. This time she made a safe voyage. In February, 1781, the *Ariel* dropped anchor in Philadelphia.

News of John Paul Jones' victories had reached America long before the captain returned. Like the French people, Americans were eager to see the daring fighter. When he appeared on the streets in Philadelphia men cheered him.

One evening, Dave Bonner and Dick Dale were at an inn. They fell to talking with some men.

"I hear that Captain Jones carried the war onto British soil," one man said.

"He certainly did," Dave agreed. "He led the only attack on a British town that Americans have made in this war."

A man with stooped shoulders and deeply-lined face spoke. "I owe my freedom to Captain Jones," he said. "I was a prisoner of the British for two years. I was freed in an exchange of prisoners after Captain Jones captured British seamen."

"He gave the British a dose of their own medicine," a man laughed.

"Indeed, he did!" Dick Dale said. "And the battle between the *Serapis* and the *Richard* was a big dose, too."

"That battle made us lift our heads a little higher," another man remarked. "We were proud of our captain and his fighting men."

Dave Bonner's face grew serious. "That battle proved that America has a navy," he said. "And Captain John Paul Jones might well be called the 'Father of the American Navy'."

"You are right," a man said. "And we Americans should never forget it. I propose three cheers for our brave captain!"

"Hurrah! Hurrah! Hurrah!" The inn rang with the hearty cheers given for Captain John Paul Jones.

Most Americans had only praise for the captain. But a few men spread lies about him.

Peter Landais and certain other men raised questions about his loyalty and honor.

Congress wanted to learn the truth about these charges. It ordered that a list of the questions be sent to Captain Jones. The captain wrote his answers carefully. He showed letters and papers to prove the truth of every statement that he made. He answered the men who questioned him with courage.

The members of Congress read the answers that the captain had written. They studied his letters and papers. And they knew that John Paul Jones spoke only the truth.

Congress showed its faith in the captain. It directed that a gold medal be made for him. It ordered that he be given the command of a new battleship, then being built.

Dave Bonner brought the news of the action of Congress to his friend. John Paul Jones received it quietly.

"I am glad that Congress has faith in my honor," he said.

"It's a great shame that your honor was ever

questioned," Dave stormed. "America has never had an officer more worthy of trust."

The captain smiled. He said, "And no man ever had a more loyal friend, Dave, than you."

The new warship was being built by the same man who had built the *Ranger*. Once more the ship builder set himself against John Paul Jones. He opposed every move that the captain made. But Captain Jones went on quietly directing the work. He ordered the changes that he thought necessary in the ship.

The work moved forward, even while the ship builder raged. Little by little the beautiful ship of seventy-four guns took shape. John Paul Jones' heart leaped as he looked at her.

Then came a blow. A French warship was wrecked in an American harbor. Congress gave the new warship to France, to replace the one lost.

"It's not fair!" Dick Dale cried, when he heard the news. "It's not fair to take your ship!"

"We are American officers, serving under Congress," John Paul Jones reminded his friend.

"It is the right of Congress to give orders. It is our duty to obey them."

"With a battleship you could have struck a real blow," Dick said.

"Now, I must strike with whatever ship comes to hand," John Paul Jones replied.

The captain had no ship of his own. But he did not cease to fight. He sailed with the French fleet against the British. He was with the fleet in the West Indies when the Revolutionary War ended.

The captain returned to America soon after the end of the war. Here, he met his old friends, Dave Bonner and Dick Dale.

"I wish we might have sailed on one more cruise against the British." Dave Bonner spoke his regret to John Paul Jones.

"I, too, wanted to strike another blow for freedom," the captain replied. "But what matters is that America is now a free and independent nation."

"And you helped to make her free," Dave declared.

"You praise me too much," Jones replied.
Dave Bonner shook his head. "No, I only do
you justice. In the years to come men will speak
of John Paul Jones. They will remember the
captain who never knew when he was beaten."

Dick Dale spoke up. "And they will remember,
too, the captain who proved the value of a navy."

"You love the navy, don't you, Dick?" John
Paul Jones smiled at his friend.

"Yes," Dick answered. "I am a sea-going man.
If America keeps a navy I'll be in it. If there
is no navy, I'll find work on a merchant ship."

"What do you expect to do, Dave?" the captain
asked.

"Like Dick, I'll be in the navy if America has
one," Dave replied. "But if there is no navy, I
shall settle in Philadelphia."

"You have not told us of your plans," Dick
said to the captain.

"My first task is to collect the prize money
due my crews. The men earned that money with
blood and suffering. I mean to see that it is
paid."

"Will you leave the navy?" Dave asked.

"I am a sailor," John Paul Jones said. "I want always to be on a ship. I hope she may be an American ship."

Soon after this meeting with his friends, Jones sailed for France. There, he spent many months seeking to collect the prize money. He secured a settlement of the claims in France.

John Paul Jones never gave up his dream of an American Navy. He believed that the young country needed a navy, even in time of peace. He spoke of the matter to Benjamin Franklin.

"America should keep a navy," Franklin agreed. "But since the war is over many citizens can see no need for one. Then, too, the country has little money to support a navy."

"That is too bad," John Paul Jones replied. "A growing nation is sure to have need for a navy. And when there is a need, I'll be the first to sail an American ship."

John Paul Jones lived in Europe the rest of his life. But he always thought of himself as an American.

Jones wrote to a friend, "I can never give up the glorious title of a citizen of the United States." He was faithful to America to the end.

John Paul Jones never spared himself. His body broke under the strain. He died in Paris, France, in 1792.

Many years later, John Paul Jones' body was brought back to America. The great captain was at rest in the land he loved.

*   *   *   *   *

The marble tomb of John Paul Jones is in the chapel of the United States Naval Academy at Annapolis, Maryland. Around the tomb are the names of the ships he commanded: *Providence*, *Alfred*, *Ranger*, *Bon Homme Richard*, *Serapis*, *Ariel*. The names remind Americans of John Paul Jones' daring deeds.

But those who know his story need no such reminder. For them he still stands on the flaming deck of the *Bon Homme Richard*. Above the roar of the guns his voice still rings clear.

"I have just begun to fight!"

Word List

academy—a-kad′ e-mi

admiral—ad′ mi-ral

Annapolis—a-nap′ o-lis

Ariel—ar′ i-el

Bahama Islands—ba-ha′ ma
i′ lands

boatswain—bot′ swan′

Bon Homme Richard—bon′ om′
rich′ ard

Chesapeake Bay—ches′ a-pek ba

commissioner—ko-mish′ un-er

commodore—kom′ o-dor

continental—kon′ ti-nen′ tal

convoy—kon′ voi

Edenton—e′ d′ n-tun

frigate—frig′ it

grenade—gre-nad′

independence—in′ de-pen′ dens

lieutenant—lu-ten′ ant

Nassau—naas′ o

navigation—navi-ga′ shun

Nova Scotia—no′ va sko′ sha

Pallas—pal′ as

Philadelphia—fil′ a-del′ fi-a

Providence—prov′ i-dens

quartermaster—kwor′ ter-mas′-
ter

Rappahannock River—rap′ a-
han′ uk riv′ er

Revolutionary War—rev′ o-lu′-
shun-er-i wor

Scarborough—scar′ bu-ru

Serapis—se-ra′ pis

Tobago—to-ba′ go

traitor—tra′ ter

Vengeance—ven′ jans

West Indies—west in′ diz